A CREATION B

KATHY ACKER • ALAN MOORE • PIERRE GUYOTAT • CLINT HUTZULAK
ADELE OLIVIA GLADWELL • AARON WILLIAMSON • SIMON WHITECHAPEL
STEWART HOME • JAMES HAVOC • GERALDINE MONK • JEREMY REED

D U S T

A CREATION BOOKS READER

ISBN 1 871592 44 5 • PUBLISHED 1995 BY CREATION BOOKS • A BUTCHERBEST PRODUCTION
COPYRIGHT © CREATION BOOKS AND THE INDIVIDUAL AUTHORS 1994 • A CREATION ORIGINAL
CREATION BOOKS 83 CLERKENWELL ROAD LONDON EC1 UK TEL: 0171-430-9878 FAX: 0171-242-5527
DESIGN: BRADLEY DAVIS • A BOOK EDITED BY JACK HUNTER AND DEDICATED TO DENNIS HOPPER

DUST

A CREATION BOOKS READER

INTRODUCTION: APOCALYPSE 451

In 1989, Alan McGee of Creation Records and myself formed a book publishing company, Creation Press. Our initial manifesto was 'the crucifixion of modern literature, and the resurrection of the imagination', and our initial publication, James Havoc's *Raism* – an infantile litany in praise of Satanism, completely devoid of so-called 'literary' merit – seemed to fulfil that premise admirably. Certainly, those few 'normal' people who encountered this artefact were suitably united in their scorn and derision for it. Our course was set.

While our 'classics' series was fundamentally an ironic concept – for example, would any 'proper' publishing house have included the works of H P Lovecraft in their 'classics' list, despite the fact that his work is light-years beyond the drivel paraded in 30-year-old translations by Penguin and their obsolescent ilk? – we were also, in all innocence, compelled to liberate certain proto-surrealist authors from the sexless confines of corporate publishing formats. From Isidore Ducasse to Williams S Burroughs, a chain of incendiarists who have detonated language exists, and whose work may alone endure the impending holocaust.

Meanwhile, our commitment to imaginative extremes persisted. Branded in 1992 as 'politically incorrect' and ridiculously linked to a 'satanic underground' by a sadly ill-informed mainstream journal – which resulted in a visit from plain clothes police – we were in fact already making available the work of fundamentally oppressed 'minorities' – the disabled, black women, AIDS sufferers, alcoholics and 'mad' people – which the larger, covertly fascistic publishing houses would never countenance, either deeming them 'unmarketable', or their work devoid of 'literary value'. While these dying corporations struggle to perpetuate such ludicrous concepts and their risible 'literary' empire, investing tens of thousands of pounds to shovel hollow non-entities (you know who you are) into the public eye, Creation is dedicated to celebrating the work of visionaries, deconstructivists or revolutionary plagiarists, writers of true genius such as Alan Moore, Pierre Guyotat, Jeremy Reed, Stewart Home and Aaron Williamson. This is the age of Lucifer rising – what Aiwass said to Aleister set the timer on a millennial conflagration in whose fractal fallout we may finally glimpse the return of the word to the womb. Brion Gysin's assertion that to liberate the word we must first erase it is now more imperative than ever.

Though Alan McGee has long since departed, and Creation Press and its affiliated imprints have imploded to re-emerge as the globally-distributed Creation Books, our manifesto remains intact. If there is ever a Creation 2000, it will bring you only dust, ossified thunderbolts, cave daubings, displays of entrails, ophidian sigils etched on human hide. Apocalypse 451 – the immolation of the word – is now five years on and counting. Poetry, pornography, pulp and plagiarism are gold to us; we support unconditionally the Neoist Alliance, the Kopyright Liberation Front, the E.L.A. and all other active service units dedicated to the assassination of the assassins of liberty. Death to the false prophets, to the priests, to the gaolers and the whalers, to the bankers, to the liars, to all the time-wasters and those who fear to burn on 451 time.

Are *you* ready to crucify?

— *James Williamson, Red Lion Square, 1994*

DUST

A CREATION BOOKS READER

KATHY ACKER

I BECOME A MURDERESS

Intention: I become a murderess by repeating in words the lives of other murderesses:
I become a murderess.
I'm born in the late autumn or winter of 1827.
Troy, New York.
My childhood is happy, and my parents allow me to do whatever I please as long as I, by my actions, don't infringe on their high social standing. My father is a great and wealthy man, a tall man, whom I look up to. As a child, among my dolls, I feel safe. I will never die. No one can hurt me. My mother, my father, my two older sisters, my younger sister, and my brother often ignore me, or promise to love me, give me a present, then don't; and I cry. My name at this time is Charlotte Wood.

I don't remember any of my childhood before I was 6 years old when I started learning to read. My eldest sister marries a baronet and lives in England; my second elder sister marries a doctor and moves to Scotland. I'm an obedient child: I stubbornly do what my parents and their associates want me to do. I hallucinate. I climb trees, stick needles up the asses of young boys. I hallucinate that the Virgin Mary wears black leather pants and a black leather motorcycle jacket, she climbs trees, she doesn't give a fuck for anyone. (I call up D in Los Angeles do you want to sleep with me with me when and where there why don't you spend a few days with me I'll call you tomorrow. No call three days later I'm maniacal I have to see D I don't know him hello I've got a ride to Los Angeles lie I'm not sure I know where we can stay should I not come up come up. We don't touch talk about anything personal until we get to motel never talk about anything personal spend night together I have to be at Irvine in the morning I'm busy call me Friday. Do you want me to call you yes. I call Friday call Saturday Sunday this is Kathy O uh do you want to spend a night with me again are you too busy I'm too busy uh goodbye have a good time in New York uh goodbye.)

When I'm 16, I board for the next two years at the Female Seminary in Troy, the school my elder sisters went to. The school sits by a large lake, or ocean; I spend my free time staring at the blue then green then white water. I want to be a mermaid: I swim under the heavy water with my legs together; the heavy muscles in my arms move the rest of my body. I want someone, a man, to walk up to me while I'm standing on a stone terrace, put his arms around my shoulders, his hand brush the hair off my forehead. While I'm at school, I meet the only love of my life. He is honest with me, as intelligent and paranoid as I am. My father forbids our marriage because my lover's family has insufficient social connections. When my (adopted) father suspects I've been sleeping with my future husband, he slobbers over me. Rape. My parents take me out of the Seminary, 1846, and return me to their home in Quebec.

I'm 19 years old, I meet Lieutenant William F. A. Elliot, eldest son of a baronet, who loves me, and, with the help of my parents, forces me to marry him. I have to get married. My new husband plans to take me to New York to England but I'm no longer safe. I change my woman's clothes to man's clothes, roam through the streets of New York. My parents, my husband, and I have locked me in a prison and I'm unable to fuck anyone. England is worse. Europe is worse. Scotland France Italy. These are the first signs of my madness.

Despite my two children (I fantasize D calls me that's impossible I fantasize he reads my letter to B he finds out decides he likes me we're both in New York or Los Angeles he undoes my black velvet cape, puts the palms of his hands over my nipples, rubs his hands quickly up and down his hands swerve around to the centre of my back he pulls my body against his body I begin to open my stomach he leads me to a hard bed lays down his stocky body under me) I leave my husband, I decide, I get out, leave my children out I go back home to America. My maid Helen comes with me. I hate everyone, I want to kill everyone, a rich famous man at a hotel in New York City sees me, I know what he wants, I go back home. The man has a lot of influence. My parents hate me, they drive me out of their house in Quebec, I've left my husband, I have no right to leave a man especially a man who loves me, I'm weird, I'm not a robot. Get the hell out, get the hell out of here. Do what I want. Get the hell out everywhere. Fuck them. Fuck them shit up their ass.

I have no money I'm on the street I'm dying no one's going to help me they step on me I puke I cause whatever happens to me I'll get the fuck out of here.

On the boat back to New York I have paranoid delusions: I believe that the man who is staring at me is not staring at me out of desire, lust etc. Spies haunt my footsteps at every hour of the night. I allow the man to talk to me so I can find out who my husband my parents has hired him to spy on me. Fuck me. I don't love this man; in the future I will never love him. I have a paranoid delusion I'm revenging myself on my parents. I'm escaping. I become crazier.

I give a party for my doll.

In Albany: I'm 23 years old; my lover tells me I'm beautiful and intelligent. I can't speak to anyone else but him. After skulking in the streets of Troy, I force myself to move to Albany, New York where I'll be freer. I'm constantly alone; I have no one to talk to. There's no one to whom I can be myself. The people who live in Albany hate me; they don't notice me, I'm in disguise, they talk solely about me when I can barely hear them. (I sneak down to the dark green hall to the edge of the doorway of my parents' bedroom I'm supposed to be asleep my father's telling my mother I'm bad and worthless child I can barely hear what my parents are saying.) I have to buy a pistol I scare my new maid so much she swears out a warrant for my arrest. Everyone hates me they just want to fuck me they don't want to fuck me. The cop finds me with my new lover; my lover gets me out of jail. No matter where I move in Albany everyone talks about me. I force myself to move back to Troy. Seclusion.

25. Not 25.

To escape my parents, I tried to fuck whoever I wanted, lean on a number of people; I become more closely imprisoned. I don't want anyone to tell me what I should do. I don't want anyone following me around, secretly gossiping about me, because I'm not also a robot.

In Troy I learn not to talk to anyone, even my maids, I make my life-long plans in secret. I travel to Boston, then to England, back to my beloved husband. My lover follows me to Boston, he puts his arms around the upper part of my body where are you going I'll take care of you I love you I'm the only person who can take care of you he's tall and thin grey hair I don't care who he is I don't care what he looks like his hand swings down the side of my thin body into the waist the broad spread of my ass I don't know what I look like skin separates from skin in my cunt the skins below my navel around my navel reveal a hand curves around the edges of the soft skins.

He takes my left hand places it below his cock on softer skin his hand rests above my hand his cock rises above his hand I shape move my hand around his skin he begins to moan I hear body rolls side to side I squeeze my hand in out I feel his hands grasp the turns of my shoulders push me down along his body lies over my body so that his cock moves in and out of my mouth between the opening of the skins I form a long narrow tunnel I begin to move my thighs up.

(I come out of the bathroom buttoning my pants I ask him to put on the T.V. my left hand touches his shoulder he suddenly turns toward me I've wanted him to turn toward me quickly I feel wet lips tongue in the centre of my mouth the sudden change from dream-fantasy to reality makes me unable to react he lifts my body on to the bed I feel his tongue enter my mouth the sudden change from fantasy-dream to reality makes me unable to react we both lie on our right sides I in front of you your cock touches the lips of my cunt enters the wet canal your arms tightly clasp my body around the waist warm fur up down my spine your cock slips out I bend my body until my hands almost touch my toes though I lose warmth of your skin I can feel your cock moving inside my skin skins I can begin to come the muscles of my cunt begin to move around your cock my muscles free themselves swirl to the tip of my clit out through my legs the centre of my stomach new newer muscles vibrate I'm beginning to come I don't know you.)

These are my insanities: I tell people I see on the street my neighbours are conspiring against me. I arm myself with pistols, threaten my enemies I'll rape murder them. My neighbours are a band of burglars who're planning to rob me. One of them has stopped all navigation on the Hudson. I hold a magic cork in my mouth which will accomplish everything. As the sun comes up each morning, I wander around the streets of Troy in disguise. I can appear to be sane (a robot).

I will never again write anything.

My only friends are the poor unwanted people of Troy. I hate the rich shits, will do anything to destroy them. I'm not political. I buy my meagre groceries from a grocery-saloon keeper, an Irish bum, Timothy Lanagan, who has a wife and 4 children. I know that I'm drinking too much beer and brandy, I'm too close to myself to think clearly about my degradation, my unhappiness, I'm scared all the time. I don't know what to be scared about. I love I don't love I hate I don't hate I'm scared I'm not scared I kill I don't kill. I'm beginning to learn who my enemies are.

One day the spring of '53 I'm at a dance in the Lanagans' booze-parlour I've learned how to speak the correct language one of the disgusting men insults me. No one believes he insults me. I don't know anyone I can really talk to. The Lanagans' filth ask me to leave. I'll show them. This time I'll revenge myself. I tell my gardener to ask the Lanagans to lend me two dollars. My gardener's thinking of killing me I ask the Lanagans myself for the two bucks they don't have any money they're starving I know exactly what's happening. I go back home. (I dream I return to New York I'm going to miss an important meeting of radicals in the middle of St. Mark's Place I sit in an uptown apartment stare out a window of course I miss the meeting I wander into the church when it's empty night.)

Two hours later I walk into the Lanagans' back room tell the Lanagans and the mysterious men the truth: my husband just had a railroad accident. I know exactly what's happening.

Two hours later I walk into the Lanagans' back room. The Lanagans are eating. I ask the Lanagans for an egg, and Mrs. Lanagan gives me the egg and a peeled potato. I invite her and her sister-in-law to drink beer with me. I know I'm a drunk. I'm clever, this is my plan:

I ask Mrs. Lanagan for sugar they refuse I just bought sugar I ask Mrs. Lanagan to put powdered sugar in my beer she brings back powered sugar in a saucer, two glasses, some beer. I ask Mrs. Lanagan for enough beer to fill the glasses to the brim I now have the sugar bowl in my hand. She leaves gets more beer. I spoon the sugar and arsenic I bought ten days ago to kill rats in the beer. Mrs. Lanagan notices powder on the top of the beer. It's good to drink. Lanagan calls his wife to mind the store Lanagan drinks the untouched beer. The sister-in-law drinks her beer. Two hours later Mrs. Lanagan tells me I've killed her husband and sister- in-law. She tells me to go home.

I feel angry. I've forgotten how to feel. I feel like I've done what I wanted. I feel elated. I've succeeded forgetting my parents. (I awake between 11.00 and 1.00 for a half hour to an hour clean up, talk to friends, eat, spend an hour on the beach, exercise, work for the next 8 hours taking 3 or 4 short breaks, eat a quick meal, drink wine or play chess to calm myself, fuck or don't, fall asleep. I speak to almost no one because I find it difficult to find people who will accept my alternating hermitage and maniacal falling-in-love. My style forces me to live in San Francisco or New York. I don't want to learn to drive a car I love cities I have to be sure I keep working hard in a large city.) During my childhood I give ample signs I'm wild, unlike my parents and other people. I run away with a gang of gypsies from my family's estate, my father is heavy dull I'm meek my mother's beautiful I elope with one of the grooms. I have gold hair, large blue eyes, I'm always laughing. I'm very tough. Because I won't stop being a tomboy, my parents decide I have to get married. I want to get married to get away from my parents do whatever I want to do. I'm born poor St. Helen's, the Isle of Wight. 1790. As a child, I had hardly any food to eat. My parents go to the work-house; I become a farmer's maid. The shits begin to tell me that if I don't become humble, respectful, I have to have security... I'm going to rape you you need security... I become chambermaid in a hotel. I know better.

They take me to jail. My lover who has kept me in the white house by the river never appears to help me. The Troy Female Seminary where I went to school announces in the local newspaper that Charlotte Wood lives in England. I'm Henrietta Robinson. My brother visits me in prison, due to the uproar, shaking, I'm not his sister. I wear a veil. I try to commit suicide but the shits save me. How do I get the vitriol? They make me confess the truth.

(I live quietly I change my way of life I eat grains vegetables some dairy products because I have an ulcer I'm too poor to see a doctor about once a month I fall in love with someone at the same time I live with Peter who I love I rarely form friendships I deal awkwardly with people I fall in love with.)

I'm born poor St. Helen's, Isle of Wight. 1790. As a child I have hardly any food to eat.

I'm still a child when I see my father and mother dragged to the local poorhouse, I walk alone on the city streets an old man stops me asks me if I need help I run away a dark man sticks his hand under my sweater touch my flat chest a local farmer takes me in general maid. Three years of shit I have to be tough I learn fast. I know I have to get myself what I want: The fuck with the farm-life I vanish.

I walk through a black world if I want something I have to get it. These are my next jobs – before I begin to do what I want: assistant in millinery place in the West End of London where I get fired for sleeping with a workman, I learn I can't sleep with who I want until I get enough money; I almost starve; hawk oranges in the gallery of Covent Garden theatre; become the mistress of a wealthy army officer. I'm too insecure, I'm still almost a slave, I'm not yet fully planning every step of my future life, but grasping on to this man who can feed me and clothe me and hold me warm.

I make my first mistake: I become too calm I identify too much with this man who stops me from starving. I become confused, I forgot my ambition and the ambition becomes misplaced: I have no clothes so I want more clothes; I think I can do what I want without fear of starvation so I order my lover around. I'm learning about lies. (I wear men's clothes, jeans cut an inch above the hair of my cunt I hold the ' jeans up with a studded brown leather belt when I sit on my waterbed where I write the material of the crotch of the pants presses against my cunt lips I'm always slightly hot I masturbate often when I write I write a section 15 minutes to an hour when I unbuckle my brown leather belt either unzip my jeans and/or squeeze my hand between the cloth of the jeans and my abdomen the lower palm of my hand masturbating calms me down maintain a level energy I can keep working the last two days I haven't wanted to fuck P because D hurt me I wear men's clothes jeans cut an inch above) I act too much like a man, I seem too forceful; despite my beauty my lover leaves me. I'll give you 50 pounds a month, I need more, you spend too much money, you don't save up enough money. I look at myself in the mirror I don't understand whether I'm beautiful plain or ugly I have to use what I see as an object make it as attractive as possible to other people. Now I'm two people.

The second step of my success begins in hell. No one notices me despite my beauty and intelligence; I try to teach myself politics and philosophical theory but I begin again to starve. No one can get me down; I'll show the creeps. I'm wandering in hell the streets stink of shit

I want to be able keep doing new and different actions I can't find how, the dogs eat the limbs of living humans and howl. Robbers mingle with the corpses of rich men and no one denies the rich the aristocrats anything. I decide to become servant to the madame of a brothel patronized especially by foreign royalties and noblemen forced to flee the enmity of the revolutionary governments in their own countries. The social bums, as long as their vision isn't annihilated by starvation and fear, usually known more about the ways men operate and kill in a city, than do the wealthier. I go straight for the information, the knowledge, I'm curious; I'm too vivacious charming dazzling to be fired. I hide my ambition then my knowledge behind this new front. Fuck them, I don't have to pretend to be humble and sweet. The only men I meet are the servants of aristocrats, not the aristocrats themselves.

The Duc de Bourbon one night tells his valet Gay that all beautiful women are stupid. Gay protests, mentions me, does His Royal Highness want to meet me? I've somewhat attracted a near relative of of Queen Victoria and an earl, but I'm not sure of them. This time luck favours me. I meet the Duc de Bourbon in the house in Piccadilly and become his mistress. Almost the entire rest of my life I devote to His Royal Highness, who I do not love, but use. Intellectually, I don't know if I can love anyone. I want what I want if I let myself become involved with a man his socially-made power over me will make me merge with him. I'll lose myself, amy ambition. Perhaps at some times I love the Duc de Bourbon, but at every moment I have to tell myself I'm using him, I'm separate from him, so that I keep our powers at least equal. His Royal Highness, like me, is ambitious, and I know how to play someone who is like me.

First, I have to insure that I'll never again hawk winkles in Covent Garden theatre, work for a fat imperious prostitute in any house, spread my legs, watch women smile flirt with men I know they hate I always try to look young that's the only way I can keep my lover I'm 23 years old I look at pictures of myself when I'm 20 so I know how to compose my facial muscles so I still look like I'm 20 I do a strip to keep the muscles under my skin tight and smooth why do you ruin yourself this way I'm too old to sleep with a woman I'm getting older I'll stop being beautiful my intelligence can't influence His Royal Highness unless it's backed by a strict education; I have to force His Royal Highness to respect me and need my advice about his personal and political affairs.

My goal: to enslave the Duc de Bourbon so I'll be safe, be part of the court aristocracy, so noble men and women will ask for my opinions, especially the men, I can kick them in their asses for the rest of my life. No one will look down on me and starve me again. The Duc de Bourbon laughs at my charming desire to study: I learn French, Greek, Latin the expertise of a university don:

I have to learn to use my defeats. I never again become defeated. About the Duc de Bourbon: My name is Sophie Dawes. He is married. A reversal in the politics of France restores to him his vast ancestral possessions and political powers. By this time, I am the only member of the royal set who can influence him, who can please him, who has his trust. He returns home to Chantilly, his palace: he tries to explain to me that recent upsets in the French Government force him to live quietly with his wife and to abandon me, his mistress. He's a tall slender man, and man whose subtle and quick intelligence in hindered by his belief in the restrictive morals of his ancestors. He's frightened of being alone and being disliked. I become scared of again starving and of being without him. I show him he's blind: he'll never again feel the touch of my hands inside his thighs, he'll live alone, not even knowing if his abandonment of them helped his political career and the affairs of the Country. I love him more than I ever have or will. How can I tell? (remember)? I'm scared, I'm no longer beautiful: I'm tall and heavy, my features are large, slightly red. I can only rely on my wits, like any man.

What happens? I enter the palace, Chantilly; the Duc de Bourbon subjugates his poor wife; for 14 years I rule that part of the court aristocracy. I want both men and women to love me. I don't have enough control the women look down on me; they sense I once worked in a whorehouse, I'm not married, fuck them, I'm not a robot, I want to love them, I want to walk into a room, watch them flock to me so I can kick their shit up their assholes. When you've come from the gutter, done everything you can to stay alive, rich and famous, you don't forget anything, you get a photographic memory. I tell the Duc de Bourbon I want to ease his wife's position at Chantilly. I now make use of the ambiguity of my position at Chantilly to raise my social position in the court. I bribe an old watchmaker 10,000 francs to tell Adrien Victor de Feuchères, a young nobleman in the Royal Guards, that I'm the daughter of the Duc de Bourbon and have a dowry of ten million francs. I have to get married.

The next day I marry Adrien in London; my lover gives my husband a position in his household. I meet the King and Queen of France. I entertain royalty; I'm 29 years old, I'm not beautiful; I own jewellery, horses and carriages; my husband purchases two estates for me because his other property, when he dies, descends to the nearest blood relation; I visit the Court several times. What does this wealth mean to me? I can no longer remember any of the events of my childhood. One of my brothers dies in a workhouse infirmary. I'm able to do the work I want and have the men I respect discuss my and their work among each other and with me. I care about the economic aspect as much as I care about my fucking with men. I often sleep with my women friends, I lie under heavy quilts, my body next to my friend's body; I place my lips on her lips, I put my left arm under her soft head, dark curling hair, my right arm around her left shoulder my hand touches her back. Her thousands of long arms draw my body against the front of her body so my head rests under her head in the hollow of her neck and chest. My eyes are closed. For a long time we lie still like this we both rest at the edge of sleep. I don't have the leisure to be monogamous. Other women sleep around our bed watch us. My sex operates as a mask for my need for friends.

I make a major mistake. I stop trying to gain more power; for me, respectability. My husband realises I am the Duc de Bourbon's lover not his daughter; censures the Duc de Bourbon, god knows for what the fucking moralist; writes to the King; resigns his commission in the Royal Guards; and disappears. The King informs me I'm no longer allowed in Court. The Duc de Bourbon tries to console me. Give me more money. I spend almost all my money trying to reobtain my right of entry to the Court; I can find no way to do what I want. This is the first time anyone has absolutely denied me (I remember). I can't understand, deal with the situation. I begin to become monomaniacal and learn the nature (nonnature) of reality.

The duke, like most men over 70, is attracted to young charming women. I'm neither young nor charming; he could abandon me any day, tell me nothing until the disaster occurs. I discharge almost all the servants who are loyal to the duke; I substitute my servants who check all his mail. The duke might revenge himself on me for his imprisonment by secretly making a new will and dying. I fight. I have to get as rich as possible.

If I make the duke leave me all his money, the duke's relations will begin a series of lawsuits which will, at best, tie up the money while I'm alive. I ask the duke to make the younger son of the Duc d'Orleans, the cousin of the King, his heir. (1) The Duc d'Orleans is almost impoverished, will gladly help me to obtain the money if he can get part of it. Poverty destroys stupid scruples. (2) The royal family will help settle the will, as relatives to the Duc d'Orleans, and they'll grant me the right of entry to the Court. The duke refuses to make a d'Orleans his heir. I force him to. Am I doing wrong? The duke secretly plots to flee Chantilly; I find this out; he hides in the corner of an old room, his frail body shakes when he sees me. He tries to bribe me to leave him 50,000 pounds. I watch myself destroy him, I become more scared that he'll take possession of me. I'm often too frightened to fuck, to let myself open myself. Masturbate.

The King informs me he is graciously pleased to receive me at his Court. Louis Philippe becomes King of France. One night the duke and

I are dining at the Château de Saint-Leu, a present the duke has given me. (I don't like or don't care about most people; when I decide I like someone I over-react I scare the person. I know I'm going to over-react, no one I like will like me, I try to hide my feelings by acting like a sex maniac, excuse me, would you like to sleep with me, I begin to think I'm only sexually interested in the person. I chase the person, I'm vulnerable, I act as tough as possible to cover my vulnerability. I don't know how to tell people I like I want to be friends, sit next to them so I can smell the salt on their skin, try to learn as much as possible about their memories, ways of perceiving different events. Because most people I like don't like me, I'm scared to show them I like them. I feel I'm weird. I don't comprehend what signals a person I like gives indicate the person likes me, what signals indicate the person dislikes me). The duke, two gentlemen-in-waiting, and I play whist; the duke calmly tells Gay, his head valet, he wishes to be woken at 8.00 the next morning, and retires to his bedroom. I feel restless. I see a warm friend of mine, a woman servant, who tells me she knows the duke has made a secret will which disinherits me. Where's the will? She shows me the will. If I destroy the will, the duke will eventually discover its disappearance, make a new will. I can stop this only by killing him. My friend understands. We sneak quietly to the duke's bedroom, we use two of the duke's handkerchiefs to strangle him in his bed, sailors' knot my nephew taught me when he stayed with me at Chantilly; we move the huge heavy bed the duke sleeps in two feet away from the wall, hang the thin body by the handkerchiefs from the fastening of the strong French window, the feet of the duke 30 inches above the floor. The duke seems to have committed suicide.

My name is Laura Lane. I'm born in Holly Springs, Mississippi, in 1837. My name is Adelaide Blanche de la Tremouille. I K A, fall in love with D; D burns me.

When I'm 16 I marry William Stone who owns a liquor store in New Orleans. He likes to think of himself wearing black leather, studded flashy boots, he drinks, shoots bullets into the walls around me, I learn to handle guns, I have to do what I do, into the chicken coops, he threatens he wants to kill someone. I learn about that fantasy. He holds a gun to my head when he's drunk so he can watch me throw fits. I love my mother; we decide to go to San Francisco together. First fantasy.

I marry Colonel William D. Fair, a lawyer. Lawyers tell you what's wrong, what's right. The Colonel shows me if I don't do what he wants, he'll kill himself. Phooey. Two years later, he shoots himself in the head with a Colt six-shooter. Am I supposed to feel guilty? Second fantasy.

My mother, I, my six year old daughter Lillias, with three hundred bucks, head for the silver, Virginia City, Nevada. Head for the money without a man. I have to do what I have to do. Single-handed I open the Tahoe House, make a success out of my hotel. I don't want to sit in my room, count my money forever; I got sexually burned twice. Big shit. I want more than money and fame. Third fantasy.

I meet Alexander Parker Crittenden and fall deeply in love with him. He's 46, a hawk; the first time we fuck, he holds me on top of him in bed, he's surprisingly gentle especially since he's a bad fuck. Has no idea how to touch the skin around my clit, give me pleasure. Fourth fantasy. My mother believed that marriage, both marriage and monogamy, cause the people involved to lose their ambition, wits, and sense of humour, especially the people who have less of the power. My mother's neighbours son showed my mother they would accept no bastard weirdos in their robot town; my father, a well-to-do Englishman, flees with me to England.

On April 9, 1895 I marry a man who I've met only once before my father's paid him to marry me because I'm a bastard.

The story of seven years: The early 1860's in Virginia City, Nevada. 30,000 people shove to get themselves as rich as possible. I don't want to be rich and famous. You can kill whoever you please as long as you've got a reason. Make one up. Wild dogs howl beneath the gangrened limbs of the old. Respectable has no real meaning. I'm 19 years old five feet three inches tall large dark eyes curly hair I know about music and art. Crittenden's a famous lawyer; elected to Nevada's first General Assembly; holds one of the most successful corporate practices in the state. Like me, he believes in being politically powerful, socially respectable, and rich. We're both tough; we do what we have to do; we don't believe in bucking other people, the society, unless we have to. We're both loyal Southerners who respect the ways of luxury and tradition. When some fucking Yankee runs his puke Union flag up the pole that stands outside Tahoe House, I flash my revolver, order the Yankee off the roof; no; I shoot the son- of-a-bitch.

The bastards arrest try me for attempted murder. I appear to go along with society, but that's what they are; bastards. Crittenden, my lover, has the same respect for society I've got my flashy looks. He uses his prestige and money: impanels a jury of twelve secessionists, prays aloud to Shakespeare and Jeff Davis; his silver tongue gets me off the hook. I learn about the nature of reality and love Crittenden even more. In this situation, murder means nothing.

All that matters to me is my love for Crittenden I think about him every hour I imagine I see him again he tells me he hates me I turn around in the bathroom I see his blue eyes next to my eyes I put my hands on his shoulders he closes my body with his body his skins close wild horses around my skin.

What are the sources for this insane love? In what ways is my desire to have someone I love with me connected to a desire to murder? (When I'm a child, my parents own a summer house by the Atlantic, every afternoon between 5.00 and 8.00 I walk on the sand by the green ocean, I climb up to the end of the jetties, watch the waves break as they turn under each other, not back/forth, but back/forth/under/same/time/as/ over/back/forth.) I decide I'll do anything for Crittenden. A few days after my acquittal I learn Crittenden's married, has 7 children. Crittenden convinces me to have dinner with him and his wife at the Occidental Hotel in San Francisco. I descend into slavery, I let a man drive his fingers into my brains and reform my brains as he wants. Crittenden follows me back to Virginia City; my mother kicks him out of Tahoe House, refused to let him see me; I buy a house in the rich part of town and move in with Crittenden. Crittenden invites his wife to stay in my house. Why do I let Crittenden enslave me? I'm crazy. I'm no longer interested in this. I remember my second husband; I shoot at my head with a gun.

Stop. I go from trap to trap to trap. Crittenden's still promising to divorce his wife. I follow Crittenden to San Francisco; I have more money than I need. I have more than I want.

I almost die from stillborn childbirth; I tell my husband I'm not going to have a kid again. I didn't want to marry him; I don't want him around, ruling me. Fuck all of them.

If someone bothers me, I shoot her/him. I shot that Union soldier on the roof, and Crittenden got me off the hook. Crittenden now tells me that Mrs. Crittenden's back East; he won't let her again into California. I'm his slave and believe him. I don't want to be a slave. I aim a five-shooter at Crittenden, fire, and purposely miss him. I marry this guy Snyder who's a weakling; in a month Crittenden arranges for me to get a divorce so I can return to him. He begins to furnish a house on Ellis Street for his wife who's returning from the East. (A wants to fuck E. A's sleeping with me he puts me to sleep in the attic M's fucking next door I hear A make love to E through the floor. I open the attic window climb down the roof, shimmy down a long pole, I run back to a school A tells me he'll decide between me and E; I'm better. He picks me. Next day he tells me E's pregnant, get out this instant.) Crittenden's going to get a divorce, go East with me. For the moment I'm content, I don't believe him, I pretend I believe him. I have to learn how I can co-exist with my tempestuous emotions. I'm mainly interested in myself. I buy a new gun: a sharp four-shooter. (After L at night goes to sleep he has to work the next day I think about killing him I imagine I walk up to the bed in which he's sleeping with a knife stick the knife through the left side of his body under his ribs.) On November 3 Crittenden stops at our house, I know it's the last time, I want to be tough; I won't be hysterical; I can't let the first emotions out I'm not his robot fuck. He could belong to me; I have to kill the other people he thinks he belongs to. I'll be a vegetable. (I let L hit me leave me broke without a home because I no longer want to fuck him he lives at the same time with a new lover his new lover watches him hit me makes comments about the scene. I let L tell me the only thing I'm good for is fucking, the only reason he lives with me.) I want to be rich and famous; no, I want to be able to talk with people without having them put me down.

I put on a huge velvet cape, a hat with a thick veil, my holster and gun; I follow my lover carefully silently in a hack I secretly hired yesterday, past low brown and grey buildings whose empty windows rats hover over, past women and men walking arm-in-arm as if they can. (In New York, I shaved off my hair, wore a black bishop's coat, jeans, heavy boots, so I'd look like a boy; if a man asked me the time in public, I'd kick him. I tried to meet more women, I couldn't figure how; everyone disliked me) Secretly I board the El Capitan, the opium-infested side-wheeler that's going to ferry my lover to his so-called wife. People crowd around me; they want to confuse me, gather me; I become lost. I don't like to be in a crowd of people unless I'm invisible I have fantasies I'm invisible or people rush over to me how are you darling do you want to sleep with me? The ferry docks; I rush through the crowd to see Crittenden meet his wife; bodies block me; I can't do what I want; I see Crittenden and Clara sitting on the upper deck; Clara's hands are crossed, I see a blue dress with tiny white flowers, gloves, why gloves; I think she's smiling, a stupid kid in a military uniform, Crittenden's smiling; I can't even escape into my own pretensions. I watch every moment they make. I hear a whistle, 5.50 p.m. the side-wheeler's about to return to San Francisco. I'll never see Crittenden again. (I don't know how to deal with someone I love or want to see refusing to see me, disliking me. I finally force myself to see that the people I love (some) dislike me. Even though they dislike me, I can't them; I keep trying to talk to them, I keep bothering them, make them dislike me more, me more entangled in fears/shyness. They show they hate me; I see myself sitting under the clothes in my closet; I don't see anyone; I wait for the whole to close.) I shoot Crittenden; he mutters something; I drop my gun, wait for the police to capture me. I'm hysterical start screaming louder and louder.

All the above events are taken from myself, ENTER MURDERERS! by E.H. Bierstadt, MURDER FOR PROFIT by W. Bollitho, BLOOD IN THE PARLOUR by D. Dunbar, ROGUES AND ADVENTURESSES by C. Kingston.

ADÈLE OLIVIA GLADWELL

DÉJÀ ENTENDU:
HAVEN'T WE HEARD IT BEFORE?

O, this is terrible. This IS terrible. The tears run down my face. All my histories are here. And all the things I have avoided. All here. And it is terrible. Now the tears are running down my arm. Only inside of my arm. They trace a path; what a terrible path. They reach my fingers. My fingers are trapped in my mouth trying to gauge out a route, for my word. Here it comes and what it says is terrible. The tears start up again. Now down my other arm. To the word. The word. I am crying. I am crying so hard. But the word is not quite escaping me. Why? I hold on to myself. I am open and flailing. Embarrassed. Abashed at my gore but the word cleaving. My cleavage. Mother. I said my cleavage. I meant it mama. I really meant it this time. Like the last time. But more so. More so. Rank mom. Rank, damp. Dangerous. The word is bleeding. It's bleeding. I can't quite believe it. I'm not sure I believe I wrote that. But it's really bleeding. Just like you did, mama. Just like you. With the very same rank o' hue. You. You. I mean you, now. And I can't quite believe it. Who wrote that mama? Who wrote the blood like that? Word? She wrote just like that. Lover. All your histories are here, lover. All your histories are here. All the figures that come and go, are pushed on, shoved and then embraced again in a strange malaise-ridden space. Oneiric, and they are all here. All the unwritten histories. Hysteries. Crying. I am crying now so hard I can almost not bear to. But I start crying again.

The voice. The voice. My eyes are closed. Just like her my eyes are closed. I write with my ears. I write with the voice that I once heard. Dreading to hear it again. O, love, I dread I'll never hear it again. Strain. I strain. Strain through others' words. What? What? Was that the voice. No wrong. Very wrong, love. I heard with the voice though. Self-blinded. Blind and fumbling around, until the voice. The insight. The hot oceanic insight. Yes, that's the voice. O I never thought I'd hear you again. I cry. I start to cry. Heavily. Thick as blood. Just to hear the voice. The voice. O yes! Yes! Hear. Here. The First Voice. O Love! The First Voice. Back again. Returned as if it were my last. The Last Voice. Crying. Don't cry baby. Why are you crying? Don't cry for me. I said don't cry for

FROM THE NOVELLA "ANIMUS: A LOVE STORY"

me. I am hearing the word. It's all right now. It's all right. Alright now baby.

But one day they will come. I know. I have maybe long known it. They cannot not come. It's in their History to come. It's in my hysterie, my glittering tainted ecstasies, to know they will come.

They won't come alone. No, their strategic mass will come armed; allied. If I didn't know I wouldn't know this site will be a battleground. I will stand scarecrow in the midst of this sorrowful field of conflict. Like scarecrow only occasionally frightening. Seeing the oncoming mass; quivering and itching.

They will come armed. You won't know it to see them. Weaponry looking innocuous, but I'll not dismantle my banks of defence. I might remember how I loved the mass. Spun on its bilberry flagpole like an orbiting golden ring. Once. Again.

I will hide down in the green still-water ponds behind my dykes. Could be lethal! I feel a bilious magick rise up from my spleen. I will not have a white flag; my flag will be red. By nature. And nurture. I will not have the white flag I do not own. They will tell me they smell me. We can smell you from here – they say. They will sweat and snuffle through their noses. Howl.

Bullets will be spite, scorn, threat, disregard. Blast, fire! Hitting my banks, as I spit back. I will bleed a little but my scar tissue is rapid. I hope. Bitterness will scab my wounds. I will pick the crusts, no doubt making a pretty fine mess of it. They will bleed too, quite copiously. They hold up their bloodiness; martyred, feeling like real women, able to lose a little vitality.

But the most odious by far – poison gases. Wilting, dissolving. Insidious, diaphanous, not-really-there. But I will smell them. Covert harm. I will inhale deeply. Choke a little. Familiarity! For I have given off this scent myself. Little by little – they will chip away. Guilty, guilty me. Handcuffing hormones, tears and temporality. The shout goes out – a siren. Yells bomb blast. Tirade. Each lovesong of dreams put under the microscope.

But oh no! Oh no! I forgot to remind myself. They are already here.

I told you they would come. Disadvantageous. They were always here. Staring hard at each chapter – repulsed by its dewy, hirsute skin.

They shout from my stomach cavern. We are in. We've always been in. They tell me they know my plan; my hand and have for years. Why do I dash and hide the evidence? A step back. No, a side step. I hear a crying Voice. Wounded and indignant. It starts to scream. It tears at my heart. I rip at the bosom of my dress. Tear the fabric from my breast. Let the longtime friends – now distanced and sorrowful – out. The word comes out, carried in the arms of that most precious bearer. She who always speaks. Aloud, even when she is not heard. Let the longtime friends, my lady. They still remind us. Remember me. Speak joy for us. Speak, Love.

The story is breaking up. The lines a series of dashes that no longer point in the same direction. Curls; spirals; loops; alcoves in the line. The embroidery. Which encloses and houses secrets. Like, the phlegm and the discharge and the clenched fingers and the sweat trickling down the ribcage, half locked. Many un-translatable signs; words even. Endorsing a dis-continuity; a temporal path that doubles back on its self. Swallows its self, like an onanistic serpent. Cuts its self up, precipitates its self. Sublimates its self. We watch and laugh and sigh. And she conducts this symphony of blended assent and adoration. The space between the lines, sings a musty cadence. She knows she's heard it before. The pauses for breath could be the mouth of a uterus partaking in a parturition of renewed hope. Oh god, yes! The full stop of each crazed cut-up – the death of every minute syllable and detail. To come around again. Look here it comes, darling. Get your knife and spit ready.

But, of the journey – it continues like this, as it must. Rebellious, murderous, nurturing.

Arden sent herself a letter. She often sends letters and lengthy missives to herself. If she could she would phone herself up. Chat away with an electric voice about everything and nothing. She would confess to such naughty, monstrous deeds and doings. She would admit to feelings she never thought she had, because of that limb of a telephone. Making waves; making waves with her voice. And she would tape herself. Later wonder where the hell she was, and who was that? That small electric voice talking about death and things. Small, electric, comically solemn but insistent. And she will just have to ask – but how does *she* know?

I still await Death. I offer Him flowers, bloody items, unborn scions and words. And I want Him to take. Take on. The wind blowing. Ravishment. Ravages. Bearing down, and stripping. Mostly offering Him words like eggs. I want Him to Bear them. The weight. Does He birth words? Does He smash them like china crockery and glass baubles. I shall write His words. Rapist. Some words He seems to quite adore. See how He smirks, licks His lips, mocks my fumbling.

He seems so tranquil then, but I know this solemn comfort of His hides The Tempest. The Ripping Hurt. The One Storm. The first and last. I ride it; straddle its swafe of crackling circuitry like a whore. My skirts hoisted. My sex rubbing indulgently against the rolls.
He is maddened now; fearful. And aroused. Swollen and argumentative. He is breaking up. I know this because I feel His trembling hands. I feel them. The story breaks up. Neither of us can make the syntax flow. Watch my lips. The flower is a bud, thorn, moribund petal(fallen), all at once. We are pricked by it; stained by it; enchanted and nervous. Wet with sap. The line – like a wave. Breaking, crashing. Folding back, imploding. Pealing and retracting its dermis. Spreading onto the stony beach. Cutting the breakers, housing the lovers. The destroyers and sirens. The poor mermaid's toes walk on swords and razor blades; fish flow.

We smell the salt. Almost our undoing. The saline breath of Death smeared like excreta on this love-letter-story. The presence of His semen always in my nose between the lines in the pages.

I wait upon the story. Losing it as I consume it. This is murder. No! Worse than that – rape. His skeletal mass is returning for me. I should run but I wait. If I run He will catch me. If I wait, very still, stationary – I will miss Him. Camouflage. But I can't wait. Oh I can't. I must go. The journey calls. Little egg shell pieces for my toes. Like minute crabs.

If He catches me. Oh yes. He is just draped, not a long distance off, with His arms stretched. Watching for the moment when I sidle up and hold on for dear life, just so He can see me seeing He is Nothing. Nothing. Just so I can see what's left of Him watching me search through my pages, not recognising a single blasted word. Was this me? Why do you make me realise that this is the death of me here in our rampant bloody words. But, look! Here is a thread. The Thread back to our innards. Our umbilical. I tug my wanton flesh up, stagger. Crouch, and crawl off again. I move slowly, waiting as I slither on. Loving our rabid consummation. Loving Him. Oh I love Him. I love Him. I love the distance. The space. Love. I am hungrier than ever. The Past can't return with its insanity. I can no longer dwell on the tortures of my old god. But up ahead the horizon is darkening. The anus birthing again. Many more eggs and dreams and words. Over that short, low hill He is wanking. Licking His wound thinking up new words to confound me.

Now this feels as if the journey is coming to some sort of end.

Drawn together so tightly; finely. But this is no end. But because the abecedary is confused, and confusing itself I could have lost sight of the final letter. The last letter I shall ever write. The final missive to my quasi-anthropoid child. I wonder what it will make of its mother's agraphia? Perhaps it will opine that I commenced at the wrong end, and have slaughtered its very essence; aborted its imagined substance; or deadlocked it in the most savage abjection.

But this is no cessation.

There are too many artificial but supreme glows humming like fireflies in this blind site. Humming in my Ear. She's humming – she's very close. Her proximity is a tangible thing. Like contentment; and *jouissance*.

He is genuflexing some distance away. Now, how strangely He is sat still, and composed in someone's father's fireside chair. I am viewing Him with my third eye – down the inverted end of a spy-glass-tube.
No! This is no Real end. I can dictate and translate various finales but this is no Real Full End. No. There is still the marginal desire. A margin to others and a choking fullness to me. Still the exiled plead for the momentum, the little hurt, the small ghost of the mythology. There is still the possibility that I could be or become my own worst enemy or, more dire than that, I could let them call me guilty, become so enraged I become as bad as those whom I enrage. Terrorism reigns here. It is at the root of own worlds. And my world is as terrible as yours. I hurl my

FROM THE NOVELLA "ANIMUS: A LOVE STORY"

anger back. It helps me cling on; for we are all fearful of falling.

Yes, my space still cries. No, now it softly whimpers. The baby slowly crawls and fumbles. Slowly. Where once I thought that all was speeding up; acceleration. Acceleration. Burning frightfully. Hang on. Hold tight. Jesus, but we're going so fast and falling. Plummet, and then float on and hit an air pocket. Falling. We'll hit the bottom. PREPARE.

Now I see how slo-mo we go. I see detail. The implosion that overtook, took-over from the explosion – out; now, slowly folds back like a sea slug onto itself, and how slow. Slowly. Sloth. Languor watches Him lift His crooked left hand to His mouth and wipe His lower lip. And feeds its eyes. Watches every tiny move hungrily – by degrees. Hypnotic; in ectasis. Indolently studies the saliva painted fireside sienna – slowly – glint glint flicker dazzle blinding me.

I gain further In-sight. And, I see inside that slowly – the further we go – the more – the more – the very more – it slips away. Mirage; and vast. Terribly strange, almost beautiful and vast. This is no end. We roll. Roll on.

I thought we had neared the end because my body was wrung out. I thought I had fully flooded out, fully bled – out. Drained, vomited, excreted, disembogued, secreted. Opened the sluices and floodgates. Sent myself all on its way to Coventry. I saw my tired, weary, moribund body – purging itself to a clean death by the breakers. Children ran past, then halted and pointed. Look at the strange empty lady. Look! Look! I can't – I say. But look! She's crawling. Hermit crabs come from her nostrils, small fish from her rictus lips. Look! She looks like she's drowned. Yes, drowned in myself, little boy, little girl.

But I purged nothing. Nothing to stand up on its own. All the spit, shit, blood and lymph in the world won't make something that can be, all on its own. It's just me at the daybreak. Just myself I reject and desire.

It seeped. It seeped out and no one was there amidst my detritus, my beachcombing ravages, but little fluids coagulating and disintegrating, chipped nails and a few strands of knotted hair.

But no-one being. I moved slowly, slowly and it was a terrible end I thought I was approaching. But out of this slothful temporality – highlights more to come. More? More! – He says. God was born on that day. I thought god was born on that day – but No. God just arose and turned me inside out on that day. Cleverly turned me inside out like a discarded frock. You pull it over your head, then remove your arms – you see. All the seams inside out and the frills. Inside out and there I was ready to take it all in again. Just when I thought you'd deserted me.

Waiting for the hermit. Waiting for the bait. But I was inside it. I was inside. Just an ancient old puzzle – turning and turning. I was inside. I was the bug. Others tugged me out like an oyster, but you can't take the oyster out of the girl, like that. I was the bug. The parasite. The visceral inhabitant and the crab – the baby – the foetus – the embryo – the little spark – the little spark in my eye – the little thing in Her – the little voice – the First Voice. I've birthed Him; look – I shout. I scream up from His bowels. Look! I did alright, I giggle. Strange how defunct my sight. But with my in-sight I see Him almost all right.

Slowly, slowly. Sometimes we slowly waltz. Even tango, swirl around in graceful circles. Waiting and awaiting because we cannot bear to not wait. But if I wait He won't come. If I focus on the door He won't come. Already the fine forks of the tuning prong are vibrating the fine reeds of our beings; vibrations that will increase and increase, almost unbearably.

So maybe one or both (or neither) had come to realize the worth of unrequited love. Though both are often too grand for masochism, there is in this a certain predilection for knowing abjection.

Once, years past, Arden had laid in her child's bed, and dreamt of flows of hot love funnelling into her and through her. But only Him. Now the spark to light the narcissistic love. A little madness; niggardly, petulant tears, and on and on.

And kissing a photograph, that was not quite what you desired. Urgent lips pleading the case. Yearning against the tacky surface, willing something dead to wake. A *nature morte*; a still-life more life-like than

FROM THE NOVELLA "ANIMUS: A LOVE STORY"

alive.

This beauty in death, and rejection. The swooning joy of introjection and expulsion. The surge of the expelling muscles into the dark side latrine. Flee and run – retentive and scared. Scatter like nothing. But the more she is excluded the more terrifying she becomes.

Then the Voice will shriek and laugh, as if at a bad private joke, carving down on the foundations of the resurrection like a hawk. Hear Her! Hear Her! Blind words with your Ear.

So did He come like Nosferatu, clad in a mephitic cape? The hacking black lover. The marginal incarnate. Miming all that has been unsaid, or disregarded. And she waits for him to gag-retch on her substance – but He doesn't. Only He thinks to Himself – was this really what His father had meant about crazy women? Raving divas with attitude and things?

She offers me a glass of wine. How does she know this is my favourite glass? The one with the chink on the rim and the fragile stem. Behemoth arises from the purple fumes to swamp us. As we look into our glass.

Now we are at this moment consubstantial. Besmeared by our own menorrhoea. Coagulated, we extrude it, like liver off our flailing tongues. When it comes. This I can say for I hear it in my inner ear – *ex cathedrâ*. Yes! This is almost exactly what Arden and Him feel.

This heady wine they partake of. Inspissated by the heat of our boomerang delight. Beautiful wine – he whispers. I watch its descent through the pellicle of our siamese mirror. We clink our glasses. Here's to you, my dear little tulpa. Bless you.

And this is chanted like a sacred litany. A small, grave voice monotonously tattooing the point onto conscience. Engraving herself with this evening dissertation; for she is almost believing of it.

This somewhat masochism, caused by subjective idealization and pseudo-autism. And there is the eternal black hole and this is the true lover. And this will be the true lover. And this will be the answer. For this is the state she is in. A blood lust for denouement but a failure to find the blood substance elsewhere.

So then, He is the black hole. My striving pain of waiting is the lover. Never wishing to obtain no more than I can finish. That He is not mine lover – does make Him my lover. For He is no less vague than The Lover should be. When they feel they are being true and overwhelming with honesty and integrity. Then what is true and honest, tell me? I can only use my inner ear and slippery-armed perception as the truth measure. But here in my head – I can almost touch Him, chase Him, escape Him; paint Him any shade or colour – for then I am God.

The image, the pastiche, the daydream, the nightmare. The incubus who enters in between the covers of my lies and aspirations. The shadow who draws the night for me, so He can entertain with his fury and hatred. Yes, such anger and hatred. My fictional factuals that leap and bite me. Yes, I have seen you spying on me – I see from the corner of my blind, blind eye.

Make Him real? This vehicle. This small inspirational malady that grows as the years pass. Then this is real. My ears turn in on themselves.

For I cannot reach this state as I do not know where the scratch is at. And if this means turning on the light to blissful repression then I prefer to wait. Rather then wring out my imagination and let them speculate for me on my behalf.

I will write It; my lids glued and reflective. Journey on, girl. Go boomerang on.

As I birth the frantic nightmaredreamlovestoryimmensity, I become the Mother (the Mother who launched me) in order to recollect myself. To become the she, it, she; God. As I birth it I read its swaddling cloth hieroglyphics – I peek into each corner of the next page – before I turn it – lest that page shall write its own death. Lest that page be the one massive anus of expelling everything to the point of the whole tome rotting away. I feel she would be heartbroken beyond repair by this. I am probably right. Arden would grow up a suspicious, shamed, embarrassed, closed book. So I continue to impearl the florid extravagance of her oneiromancy; so she will hopefully remain as hopeful as I can. Her self-signifying mythology; for some ages to come. Maybe she will bloom – immortelle on my upper arm. A swarm of spectral jellyfish surfacing an ocean.

Yes, the omnium-gatherum-Arden sits heavy on my shoulders. Her tough fists ball in my hair – I hear her huff, snuffle, snark, burp – down – my neck. She pinches hard, HARD – then lovingly tongues the tiny bruise marks at my throat. Twists my stomach, my breath is caught. Gloriously hysterical, I find I am caught in the fragile apparel of her tell-tell. I hear her brave, lonely, indulgent laughter – as a schizophrenic; gloriously hysteric.

And Arden has peeled every last layer of cells from my heart – right down to the voracious valve. So all there is – is valve. Now, that's all there is. Now, that's alright. Now. I am a newly-born acardius. No heart – but a sucking valve space. Every feeling she drew out with the straw of her need for being. A proboscis filching my sight from out-turning.

I am loathe to deny her. I am loath to forget her, leave her – for then she will surely damage me. And I will cruelly, oh cruelly hurt her; I feel for her, I do. Immolated on the sacrificial corners of the page; and on my bed, I attempt to lift the burden off her bloody, bloody back. But she to me is without spite, in this respect – and this is also her nature.

PIERRE GUYOTAT

╋╏╏ ╏╏ ╏⁄ ╏╏∴⊤O⊒╎⸱╎

/ Soldiers, helmets cocked down, legs spread, trampling, muscles drawn back, over new-born babes swaddled in scarlet, violet shawls : babies falling from arms of women huddled on floors of G.M.C. trucks ; driver's free hand pushing back goat thrown forward into cab ; / Ferkous pass, RIMA platoon crossing over track ; soldiers jumping out of trucks ; RIMA squad lying down on gravel, heads pressed against flint-pitted, thorn-studded tires, stripping off shirts in shadow of mudguards ; women rocking babies against breasts ; rocking movement stirring up scents sharpened with bonfire-sweat impregnating rags, hair, flesh : oil, cloves, henna, butter, indigo, black antimony — in Ferkous valley, below breakwater heaped with charred cedars, barley, wheat, bee-hives, tombstones, drinks-stand, school, gaddous, fig-trees, mechtas, stone walls oozing spattered with brains, orchards blooming, palm-trees, swollen in fire, exploding : flowers, pollen, buds, grasses, paper, rags spotted with milk, with shit, with blood, fruit-peel, feathers, lifted, shaken, tossed from flame to flame in wind pulling up fire, from earth ; slumping soldiers straightening up, sniffing tarpaulin flaps, pressing tear-stained cheeks onto burning rails, rubbing members against dusty tires ; sucking in cheeks, drooling over painted wood ; truck-squad, down in dry river bed, cutting rhododendrons, milk from stalks mixing on knife-blades with blood of youths disembowelled in onyx-quarry against central vein ; soldiers cutting back, pulling up saplings, digging out roots with studded boots ; others kicking, swinging lopsided : camel-

FROM "EDEN, EDEN, EDEN"

dung, grenades, eagle-carrion ; RIMA squad clambering into trucks, falling onto women, guns at sides, hardened members spurring violet rags clasped between women's thighs ; soldier, chest crushing baby sucking at breast, parting woman's hair pushed over eyes, stroking forehead with fingers covered in powdered onyx ; orgasm spurting saliva from mouth, dowsing baby's buttered scalp ; retracted member resting softening on shawls soaking up dye ; wind shaking trucks, sand whipping against axles, sheet-metal ; / soldiers clambering into trucks : RIMA squad, leaning against tarpaulin pressed down on necks by driving rain, buttoning up ; eyes shining in darkening shadows, fingers glimmering on belt-buckles ; goats, sweat of pursuit around bonfires soaking coats, crouching down, licking rags tied around thighs of women ; silent youth wrapped in sackcloth, propped back against driver's seat, pissing into blue enamel mug held in mutilated hand : driver, leaning back, stroking youth's forehead marked with blue cross ; youth kissing palm, wrist rippled with veins, swelling with alcoholic blood ; half-track caterpillars grinding stones thrown onto track by wind ; soldiers dozing ; dye-stained members curled against thighs, dripping drops of jissom ; driver of truck crowded with males, animals, bundles, spitting black saliva, wasp-sting swelling cheek, swollen half-closing eye, pockets crammed with black grapes : tanned head of old man, reddening under white hairs, shaking against sheet-metal, under gear-stick : with hobnail boots, driver, black saliva drying on chin, crushing, pulling immaculate locks from occiput, against metal beaten, from below, by cracked stones kicked back ; / at camp, soldier : « dogs! wash out my trucks » ; / females hanging out babies' rags on bushes ; / males setting up tents beside rubbish ditch : sludge of rotting meat, vomit, glimmering, rosy, under lifeless reeds bending ; soldiers pushing back, with butts of rifles, women laying babies down in tents ; kicking, punching haunches of males bent over unrolled tarpaulins ; RIMA squad pushing into den hollowed out under platform of camp in onyx vein ; faces heated, arms, legs swinging, bottles thrown against walls : glass splinters falling back into darkened circle pricking, sticking to hardened members shaken out of dungarees ; beer, wine — cut with bromide — splashing over shoulders, bare breasts of waiter ; RIMA squad rolling, vomiting in corners ; waiter, greasy shorts slipping down loins, barefoot, tattooed, on ankle, with woman's breast, trampling on floorcloth ; edging around counter, pushing cloth alongside lips of vomiting soldiers ; / two males tying up animals behind tents ; children, arses caked with crusts of dung, sitting on grass eroded by salt, panting, foreheads covered with dust, heads leaning lifeless on shoulders, eyes, violet-hued, watching erection of tents ; soldier with curly brown hair, mouth crammed with black meat swelling pock-marked cheeks, squatting down, soiled member bouncing inside pants, beside small girl, stroking neck, hand moving down under rags covering throat, groping around breasts, under armpits : girl's eyes closing, head touching soldier's wrist smeared with grape-juice ; grey drool of hunger running from girl's mouth onto cheek, wetting soldier's fist ; / gust of wind lifting up, over mounds of excrement, pages of comics torn out by hands of soldiers crouched over ditches, forcing out tense, burning shit after forays of rape : papers sticking to fronds of date-palms, stench of defecated grape-juice washing over lieutenant's zerriba : lieutenant, crouching, naked, in tub of lukewarm water streaked with rays filtered through lattice, whistling, medallion balanced on tip of tongue, neck-chain held on mounds of swollen cheeks, purplish glans touching grape-tinted foam, farts bubbling at sides of bronze tub, forcing rhythm of whistling ; / soldiers — on mainland : dance-hall bouncers —, in fading light, prowling around tents, untying thongs, crawling on sand, tent-flaps rubbing over backs riddled with scabies ; males, females, nerves phosphorescent, huddling together around candles, youths, ears buried, chewing raw semolina straight from sacks ; children pulling aside, with pinched lips, clenched teeth, rags covering, containing breasts of women, licking half-chewed flour from lips of youths ; soldiers, tugging at girls' naked legs ; father grabbing candle ; curly-haired soldier, rolling black meat in vermilion mouth, unsheathing dagger : soldier's hand, quick, covering vulva buried under scarlet rags, grabbing, pinching ; soldier pulling thigh, drawing sleeping girl closer : girl sliding over sand towards tent-flaps ; two soldiers, one scalped on temple by eagle's beak after rape over crowded nest, other sweating gall, dungarees rolled up over shins flecked with salt, holding down, tying up father throwing lighted candle at soldiers' hair ; curly-haired soldier gathering girl in arms : girl sleeping, purring, hand spread open over forehead, rocked in rhythmic trot ; veiled moon casting greenish glow over bared thighs ; ichneumons, sbots, sphex hovering over soldier's member : soldier stepping over kitchen cesspool ; soldier sprinting over soiled straw, alongside kennel ; panting, gurgling — prelude to rape —, sweat oozing on bare chest, waking girl : girl gazing, into soldier's mouth panting open, at threads of meat caught in canines, lumps held back in cheeks ; soldier standing girl up, squashed against wire fence of kennel, squeezing, kissing mouth, cavities of ears susurrating with bloody cerumen ; soldier's hand unbuttoning dungarees, pulling out member ; girl sucking up meat held back in soldier's cheeks, chewing, eyes closed, hands spread out on fence ; soldier, aroused by movement of muscles from cheek to belly, bare-headed, straw-dust disturbed rising around legs, injecting girl with clear, hot jissom ; dogs, woken by wire fence creaking, springing from kennels, chains gleaming, dragging in excrement ; soldier nibbling at girl's gums, teeth pulling at threads of meat, girl's teeth covered, defended by tongue ; dogs howling, chains ringing on tarmac, paws grinding into hardened excrement ; soldier's knees gripping small waist : second orgasm dowsing girl's shoulders ; girl keeping hands clasped against soldier's sweaty loins ; fence collapsing ; soldier folding, covering girl's body ; nails scraping earth ; soldier's breath against girl's cheek sucking in, blowing out straw-dust ; girl shifting belly under grinding muscles of abdomen ; blinding — nails, spit — soldier's eyes ; soldier's secreting balls lying, cooling, on girl's thigh ; below palm-trees, RIMA squad dragging woman pulled unconscious from tent : blond soldier, forehead glowering, tears bathing eye-sockets glazed with charcoal, urine blocking jissom in glans, squeezing woman held in arms ; « screw good ; fuck hard ; watch out for brass », hands, lips, stroking, licking woman's contorted face thrown back over blond soldier's arm — oil-smudged, wine-stained ; / small girl, covered, coated with straw-dust — except on lips, vulva blocked strangulating soldier's member — whining, sniffing back bloody mucus into nasal cavities ; // woman's head hitting scarified trunk : initials, school-sums, hearts pierced with arrows, of sterile palm-tree ; soldiers, unbuttoned, sugared fists squeezing swollen members, jostling between woman's legs held apart by two fellows, tension of plexus discharged, members drooping against thighs, hugged by camouflage-dungarees ; / inside tent, soldiers sitting on father's stomach, arms, chest, rubbing blackened hair with palm of hands, farting : candle, stuck into mouth of male swooning, hissing between cracked lips ; / watchtower overlooking charred palm-grove ; Peuhl sentry, yellow iris sliding into bluish eyeball, sweat soaking frizzy hair, turning spotlight : beam beating onto sweating flesh of soldiers arched over woman ; sentry grinding member in fist, turning spotlight : beam crossing dried river bed, catching vibration, bathed by zephyr, of dusty rhododendrons : pack of jackals tearing at donkey-carcass filled with putrid liquid — flanks swinging swollen ; sentry spinning projector on chassis, beam burning into nipples palpitating pubescent, sprinkled with sugar under drill of dungarees encrusted with dirt : sweat oozing through tangled tufts ; sentry's throat, beam melting blood, pus, in razor-cuts ; member forcing starched crotch, pushing out of pants, spreading, arched, under tight cloth ; sentry, fist spinning projector towards stratosphere, moaning, yawning, rubbing thighs, seam of dungarees cutting into buttocks, against sheet-metal casing chassis ; soldiers drawing back from woman wrapped around tree-trunk ; ants, mosquitos gathering seed, jissom forced back out around exposed vulva, rag — orange flowers, on violet — sticking to groin ; soldiers walking, thighs opened, heels lightened, saliva drying on chins ; tucking away members, buckling belts, wiping gnarled hands at sides, fingers coated with antimony from woman's hair ; farting ; leaning back against ladder of watchtower, feet nestling in urine-sodden sand, lighting cigarettes taken from pockets sticky with jissom, shifting haunches : glans, detached from cotton inside pants, discharging last drops of jissom ; farts rippling from sweating arses ; sentry squatting, arse hairs caked with faeces pulling apart, buttocks spreading, pressing nostrils over holes in floor ; scent of jissom wafting up from soldiers' open shirts, mixed with whiffs of toasted tobacco rising from lips, from fingers smeared with seed ; at changing of guard, sentry running from tower, hardened glans pinched in elastic of pants, towards palm-grove behind barbed wire, dragging woman, pulling feet, beyond tree, into salt-marsh slick, lying over body — breathing stopped — spreading bruised lips of vulva, pushing in member retracting on contact with cooling flesh, kissing woman's shrivelled lips, eyes, soldiers' saliva, spat over iris, drying ; woman's vulva closing around member, squeezing, crushing ; Peuhl, cold sweat oozing from pores, coating hairs, standing up, pulling fingers out of woman's wilted locks — sweat drying in tufts, lice, fleas jumping out ; flies, ichneumons diving in, heavy with black powder from charred fringes of male palms, digging down to greenish skin of scalp —, carrying fingers to member, squeezing base, pulling at hairs caught in vulva ; secreting balls clasped in free hand, white sweat seeping : mosquitos, ants stuck in foam, between sentry's fingers ; breathing, sentry choked by salty stench ; standing up, lifting woman's hips against belly, stepping forward, legs spread, staggering, weight of woman pulling down on member, stretching skin over vertebrae of sentry's neck, over atlas, axis, sternum ; on platform of dry sand, at edge of palm grove, sentry stopping : flies, mosquitos crawling under cap, in knot of hair on occiput ; woman's legs stiffening, beating against sentry's shins ; sentry kneeling, sprawling, woman's legs unfolded, varicose veins shrivelling against sand, panting over cold belly, groin muscles, tissues of member straining ; fist striking around vulva, fingers pulling on lips, digging, under folds, into stiffened muscles ; Peuhl unsheathing dagger at hips, tracing with point of blade — bent : youths gutted against onyx wall — semi-circle around vulva, plunging blade into mute flesh, tearing, stripping, slicing muscles, nerves running from vulva into flaccid sheath covering strangulated member ; member hardened on contact with disturbed muscles, springing out, capped with bloody flesh ; Peuhl gathering, stroking, wiping member on flap of sweaty shirt ; standing up, leaning back against trunk, picking up rifle from salty platform — sand, crackling, flying up into face —, coming back to woman, rifle-butt striking face, breasts, — member recoiling red, bruised, deformed, against sentry's thigh ; crouching, head turned back, seizing woman under reddened armpits : sweaty hand slipping on cold flesh ; legs spattered with blood from mangled vulva dragging on debris of bones ; Peuhl kicking dislocated corpse into hole dug under barbed wire by jackals, onto bed of carrion, excrement ejected in scramble for spoils ; sphex, sbots, blown up in draught, assailing — antennae, stings buzzing — penis, eyes, nose, lips ; Peuhl burying head in shirt, stung by wasp beneath right nipple, dung-fly drinking seed caught in hollow of exposed navel : brisk movement of torso squashing fly in sweat between two folds of flesh ; buzzing, discharging into sweat, climbing up along fold of flesh toward hip ; Peuhl running, member smarting, hands open outstretched ; at first-aid post, two bare-chested soldiers groaning, retching, cheek to cheek ; sprawled under sink, shins bathed pink slapping in vomit, forelocks trailing in gluey mash reeking of wine ; cadet, squatting, needle jabbing soldiers' bared buttocks : two orderlies holding soldiers down on tiles ; Peuhl sitting on bench, head thrown back onto shoulder, shaking, skin mottled, teeth chattering ; penis, blood drying, protruding from fly ; nipple swelling ; cadet, member sprouting, pushing at fly stained with iodine, standing up, eyes dazzled, level with rounded swelling of cheeks, fixed on fold, stretched by erection, forming beneath belt-buckle ; two orderlies lifting up, carrying soldiers to stretchers arranged outside, beside wall of hut, on trestles ; Peuhl stung on breast, whining, bloody saliva drooling from dried lips, two threads dripping onto chin ; cadet tearing off Peuhl's shirt, shirt thrown down at feet ; handkerchief in hand, thumb stroking, forcing Peuhl's lips, teeth : cadet's member stirring in pants ... « ... farting herdsman, dozing, loins stiffened from thrusting, pumping.. slender, running through drinn.. pimply mouth.., hot bath, insecticide, tooth-comb never drawing out perfume of wool, of milk.. paste, potash, gonacrine on your lips, taste of venom sucked.. no encrusted dung of buggery on glans hardened by quivering tension of loins, bitter sweat of beasts squatting in salt... ».. : Peuhl kissing cadet's fingernails through muslin, nostrils detecting crease, whiff of dried jissom ; cadet dropping handkerchief, stroking Peuhl's bare shoulder, gathering, rolling member in palm of hand, groping inside pants, pulling, pressing testicles against folds of cloth ; Peuhl, flanks strained stiffening, spreading thighs ; standing up, pressing thighs against sink, surrendering, into fingers of cadet, hardened member : squeezed against porcelain, plunged purplish into bowl of oxygenated water ; Peuhl stepping outside hut : nest of larks hissing, hooked under palm-awning ; stroking nest, larks springing up, shitting over wrist ; squatting down, stretching out on straw kept for tortured prisoners, dozing, buttocks pulled apart by stiffened seam of dungarees ; lips, wet with spittle expelled by pulsating cheeks — knees, hams, forehead trembling —, touching blood-spots on pillow... « ...drinking rebel's blood, drinking against tortured lips, tortured shins, holding blood in mouth, running through fields of blackcurrants blazing, flooded with venom, wrist chafed by sickle-charm tied to chain, running to meadow with fishes leaping, outside slave-camp ; over hill, spitting blood into onyx basin ; other slaves, scalps caked with dung, forehead to forehead, spitting other blood : golden, blue, black ; wind spraying blood over exposed loins, clouds of excrement shadowing top of hill : under overhanging rock, soldiers blowing onto bonfire of branches built around mouth of dead woman, blowing in measured breaths, squatting, tall twisted locks sweeping over woman's breasts ; chest rubbing on fleece over vulva, skylark caught in tangled hairs ; lark singing, chest pressing against body of woman, tears springing from eyes ; hot blood trickling from ears ; excremental rain splashing over rock ; blood, in basin, burning, boiling ; young rebel, bare feet daubed with onyx powder, lips with flour, rising from earth, leaning over basin, immersed head, fists ; raising head dripping with blood, hurling raucous cry towards hills, bushes moving : lions springing out ; lions lying at rebel's feet, licking behind knees ; young rebel, scooping blood mixed with excrement in cupped hands, showering lions' manes ; around camp, women slumping against fences, soldiers' members straining towards mothers, brought from mainland, for Slave-Feast ; carrying Mother into bamboo hut, laying down on bed of poisoned straw : head, shoulders buried beneath Mother's dress, eating fruits, antelope fritters over hardened vulva : Mother sleeping, tired by journey in cargo hold, tipper-trucks ; escaping at dawn, slipping from under my body ; caught by soldiers under tower — me watching, ejaculating — pushed back onto sand by goading knees, wasp hovering at right breast, over lips of soldiers sucking at teat... »..; / pressed against kennel fencing, soldier rolling, covering girl ; cadet squatting down, lifting up soldier, gripping loins : member slipping out, soldier standing up, running off ; cadet blowing off straw gathered on small contracted body, lifting girl up in arms ; body dilating under breath, vapours, juices of cadet — hugging girl, chewing ration-biscuit, girl kissing cadet's lips, tongue collecting crumbs stuck along gums ; cadet laying girl on bed in sick-bay, bathing mangled vulva ; feverish, cheek bloated with vomit, stepping back outside, switching on lights over latrines — soldiers working on group of women —, lifting up fainting soldiers, stroking forehead of women sprawled on ground, separating native mercenaries coupling, pulling apart couples stuck firm by compression of plexus ; returning, washing under running water : hands, arms, neck, smeared with jissom, with seed ; cadet, vomit expelled, carrying out girl swaddled in surgical smock, opening tents, in turn, tipping girl's face back into candlelight ; opening tent with two soldiers holding male, filled with sand heated through by movement of limbs clutching, sweating, radiance of muscular contractions ; cadet shoving soldiers aside — standing, penis retracting beneath cotton —, placing girl at feet of female, lighting candle taken from mouth of male, pushing unbuttoned soldiers towards opening of tent — at corners of lips of female, drop of jissom shimmering ; /// in bunk-rooms, bamboo waving in dawn wind, insomniac soldiers, naked, sitting cross-legged on bedding, picking at stained members ; suspect youth, caught reading shit-smeared cowboy comic in front of tent, thrown bare-chested into command-post : cheek, chest, belly marked by hand-prints, in blood ; sergeant capping suspect's blood-stained head with empty coffee-pan ; sugar sticking to hair, mixing with blood, filling ears ; soldier on fatigue-duty, frayed dungarees stretched over arched buttocks, bringing back bludgeon, smeared with excrement, from toilet ; hitting shoulder of suspect : three blows, jaw : seven, with end of stick coated with creosote, pressing stick into suspect's fist ; driver taking spanner, crank, from truck ; spanner forcing open suspect's clenched jaw, driver unbuttoning dungarees, pissing between torn lips, pulling up suspect with three spanner strokes at throat, pushing crank through tear in dungarees, between buttocks ; other soldiers aroused, rising from mattresses, grasping, turning crank in suspect's arse ; suspect, head falling back, wet with spittle, onto shoulder, crown touching tormentor's swollen crotch, lips spitting back excremental saliva, clenching teeth onto spanner ; tip of crank forced into loins ; pulled out, bloody, by driver, thrown outside command-post, wiped clean on sandbags around perimeter ; suspect youth swooning, collapsing on mattress, unbuttoned by soldiers — spitting, farting ; with barrel of rifle, soldiers lifting up, pressing penis back onto belly : sergeant's studded boot squashing flesh ; red-haired soldier, hollow eyes, glans sprouting — caught violet between two gaping buttons —, leaning over, grabbing, tying testicles of suspect in soiled rag pulled from under bedding ; fingers stroking small neck formed at root of compressed member, junction of knotted membranes ; // suspect revived in empty guard-room, cadet kneeling, untying rag ; sentry, mouth rosy in dawn fire, walking on terrace, legs bowed, fist buried inside pants ; leaning back against palm-trunk propped up by brownstone balustrade around terrace ; stiffening legs, pulling out member ; rifle, loaders, clicking at loins, masturbating, helmet pushed back over neck, jugular vein outlined in creases of throat, tongue protruding from mouth ; two children squatting, defecating against barbed wire ; soldier levelling projector-beam towards point on horizon — dawn fire looming ; woman from tents, breasts swinging in patched silk, flowery silk sticking at pubis, haunches slumped against barbed wire, fingers scraping shit between children's buttocks, wiping fingers in sand ; red fist on white arm, slipping between wire-mesh, touching sliver of ration-bread poking from sand, intact ; soldier's rifle slipping from shoulder, barrel knocking against projector chassis ; one breast springing out of silk ; member forcing soldier's fingers ; thumb of other hand, loosened by accelerating movement of masturbation shaking, contracting shoulder, milking-arm, jerking, touching trigger ; woman, throat riddled with bullets, collapsing, head, hair fading dead, rolling onto shit-smeared wires ; jissom spurting, splashing boots, sheet-metal ; between breasts, fresh blood bubbling in globular clot ; soldier linking index-finger to trigger-thumb, squeezing member at root, pressing jissom up towards violaceous glans, catching drops in fingers : tepid, carried to lips ; children, faces, bellies, swollen behind tears, heads muffled in heated rags, pressed against pubic curls, sleeping, sobbing, thin bodies shaking, waking, crying — entrails cooling, //

JAMES HAVOC

IN AND OUT OF FLESH

Addiction is an acute form of nostalgia. It works by offering a glimpse of spur-holds on the naked moment, a chance to ride time's loop counter-clockways. It might be sparked by a thought, gesture, color, geometric configuration; its onset has the power of a straight razor slicing raw nerve endings, and we are condemned to repeat history as our only anaesthetic. My addiction was the lightning. The lightning was my boyfriend. Above all, it was my signifier for Billy.

Billy was legion, less boy than bestiary. His pelvis threw shapes and shades that snuffled, sucked the breath from he-child lungs. He always had a low caste on him, as if he were ready to tear golden strips off an angel like some third eye butterfly from a rip in the sonic fur, flecked with centuried vermilion, solarized. He imagined that every molecule in his body was a flaming star, that a million light years stretched from particle to sub-atomic particle; Billy found the curved rim of ultra-space in a beer bottle, saw Hellfire in the cleft of a woman's guts. He knew how to butcher animals, and other dead languages, and his eyes were lidded by the the hangman's shadow. He lived by gun magick, and gun magick brought Pussycat forth unto him.

One of those sweet days, Billy had awoke to a life of crosses. Just one slip of the trashman's tongue was all it took; the difference between Hellfire and honey. Now the nuisance in his ear was hissing, slithering, the mating of dragonflies in a vat of peeled mandarins, or maybe a shade-tree inmate splitting livers. Pledging allegiance to a raven sun, Billy cleaved tight to the dark side of the road. The music on his radio howled like a homicide: proclamations in black, a cross-cut saw, and the clicking of old dry bones in a passway. It was 1954.

Billy thought people shouldn't be born; he left his victims in the gutter with a stars and stripes postage stamp between their eyes and return to sender carved across their cheekbones. His one and true girlfriend, Caril, did use her cunt as a repository for odd-shaped bones. She deemed this to be the act of a true poet, and believed she had re-aligned herself with the stars. She called herself Fireskin and they held hands with lightning. Billy's skin was near completely vitrified; he

FROM THE NOVEL "LUST FOR LIGHTNING"

was aimed to get a new one. Their yelps were heard in cemeteries.

Across State, they picked up a hitcher – though Billy always said it was the other way round. Her name was Goneril and she seemed to be made out of neon, a silver rebop for the buzzards; she only became truly visible by night, and when she did she lit up the sorrowful Mid-West. Goneril and Caril soon became like sisters. They took to keeping each other's menstruations in bottles, as keepsakes and also as a kind of psycho-acid to throw in mens' sick faces.

After a while, Billy and the girls decided to form a gang called the Teenage Timberwolves. They were the few, the ones born with a paw-print on the soul. Most of the time this gang was a shell, a concept lying idle. They used it only as the gateway to another dimension: a place of the living dead, a limbo larder stuffed full of fresh skin, meat and bones to replace what the lightning burnt out.

This is what would happen: A woman was stretched out in the back of a Cadillac at the roadside, giving birth. The husband ran out in the road, flagging them down with bloody hands. Caril smiled, walked up to him, put the barrel of her cold black gun under his chin and blew off his face; Goneril took the first-born. Billy looked down hard at the delirious mother. She was nothing but a filthy criminal; death was too good for her. He kicked shut the doors, locking them, and left her to slow-fry.

When the patrol car pulled up behind, there was no sign of the Teenage Timberwolves. Cadillac corpse, engine still running on the white Buick. The driver took off his helmet and opened up the trunk. It was alive with maggots, and discharged a storm of flies. Underneath, they found a mess of Navajo bones dripping bad meat, a tyre tube stuffed with barbed-wire rosettes and ratsheads, jars of menstrual blood, some blond scalps, motorsickle chains, some razors and knives, a Teddy bear, packs of cigarettes, and a box of needles with silver thread. The other cop reached out to catch a fat, lazy fly that was circling his partner's head; his fist passed through the invisible death zone of Billy Timberwolf. *Snap!* went the teenage wolfjaws – nothing came back but a stump.

I first met them in the graveyard. This is where I would sit, especially on the stormy nights, and read the Bible out loud. They were beautiful. They told me that one of them was going to ride the lightning, and if I helped out, then I too could become a Teenage Timberwolf, cannibal jailbait with a screaming fur bullet.

I read no more.

Goneril stripped in the rain, laid flat out on a marble slab. She tugged at her auburn hair, and I saw that it was a wig. Her head and pussy had been shaved and greased so they wouldn't catch fire; we had to pin her head and shoulders so she couldn't split her skull on the gravestone. The rumbles doubled, flashes of spider-pink and a terrible white darkness in the low East. Caril chewing gum, down in the ditch communing with dirt, a greased fist up her girlfiend's cunt earthing her to the firmament. The bolt struck, diffusing its power through Goneril's convulsing body. I felt the cosmic crash in my own clenched fingers, saw it surge down her arms in cold blue, raise glyphs across her rib-cage, nipples lambent with electric power, legs jerking wide apart, turned her clean over, ivy ablaze, the fucking stone nearly split in half, her tits now buzzing like generators, sparks and steaming piss shot back into the boneyard blackness. Billy mounted her, cycle boots on Caril's shoulders, her eyes stellar, circling each thumb and forefinger into his mouth, withdrew them dripping spit and reached round to engage Goneril's nipples. A sharp crack and his forearms jolted, smell of singed scar tissue; a lattice of blue light spurted from his fingertips, up through his arms to his shoulders as if embalmed alive by radioactive cobalt, bones visible in orgasm.

I felt inside-out, helped peel Goneril from the slab, smoke-breathing, leaving behind great sheets of charred skin. Caril talking of apples and ulcers, souls spitted on ligatures of broiling dog-bone. We were immersed, as if the night's gizzard had choked over, stranding us in the gut tract of some mummified snake; the words in my brain were hook-shaped, scorpions writhing under their thin membrane, straining to find light. We had soaked up every glimpse.

In the days and nights that followed, we lived in crypts. Billy said that in the time after a storm, it was best to sleep with dead skulls, receptacles for the darkest mercies of the dew. And so they languished, seem as like poised between life and death. Their enervation seemed unholy. I decided that they were true promethean lepers, upholders of a beauty too pure for this extinguished world. A beauty caged in brimstone.

Billy likened my yellow hair to leopardskins and lightning. He said that I was a true harbinger of Pussycat, the keeper of the vanilla vault, a blonde witch so full of blonde magick that it was soaking through the crotch of my jeans. He reckoned I had fallen angels on my mind. Probably kept puppy-dogs' eyeballs stashed in a puzzle-box, orchids in a concrete claw. I was fourteen years old. When it was time to leave, I went with them gladly, but I was not allowed to touch Billy. This burned my soul.

Outside storm season, we shifted in hot shadow. One time Billy had me hold down Caril's shoulders. The motel room was scattered with chicken-

FROM THE NOVEL "LUST FOR LIGHTNING"

heads and hubcaps. Goneril had her face between Caril's open thighs, and with the tip of her tongue she was extricating perfumed bones and placing them on Caril's belly. The stack of wet bones looked like a funeral pile. Billy put a dead rat on top, doused the whole thing with lighter fuel and torched it. For a while we inhaled the sweet smoke, until the heat became unbearable and Caril had to brush away the ashes. Billy ran his tongue along the grid of criss-cross scorches. If rats could speak, he whispered, they would say there was no rat Heaven.

Way south, past a gallows turnpike, we came to a place where the soil was dust-red and unrepentant. Billy knew that a man had to suffer before he deserved the harbour of the ditch; anything less and that soil would spit back your unripe bones like watermelon seeds. Here he found a town full of menopausal bigots so prejudicial they could no longer discern him. Billy liked that area; there were things in the foothills which moved, casting shadows that resembled dung pouring from an anus. He swore to imprint the South with a livid cicatrix of his own devices, a web from which would dangle the hides of the righteous on the breeze, while he slipped, wanton, in and out of flesh, from existence to ether and back again.

We were skin-stealers, lightning-fuckers, our kitten cruise was tilted at the pit. Billy said we were prophets of a mesenteric interlude between man and wolf; our very piss was hard rain, foaming snake jetsam levelled at the hearts of the iniquitous. Our bodies stank and crawled with lice, but our souls were enthroned in lairs paved with offal, roofed with skin, walled by endless slabs of human meat. We buried heads where the moon fell.

MAUVE ZONE

I left the *Victoire* listing from the depredations of the worms, the sway of the gangrenous zodiac which had steered us through the reefs to this inferno. Immune to the narcolepsy which made vampires of the crew, I had forged a pact with immolation, sworn to blood the brine by suicide. From this night on, the black flag was my soul.

Dogs were running, their faces were my face, an effigy in primeval mud. The maidenhead of midnight hung in tatters. Sand and sea interlaced underfoot like the suture round a barbarous circumcision and from the horizon, biliously level, to the unfathomable forest reaches the sky dripped down in anguish. It was molten church glass, balm shot through with a configuration of poison stars, a fistular glyptograph for annihilation; its deepest gulfs disgorged a wash of embers by whose light I butchered my mother.

I first hacked off her fins, those black rudders whose sinews once cleaved sightless seaways to the vortex of ice which immured me; then flayed her primal carcass, the cancer finally sluiced from the ocean's jurassic caul. Her split underbelly surrendered the sacraments of my becoming: shards of gaze from a tombstone mirror, the spectre of cannibal rabies, a last reverberation of dead names in subaquatic nuptial chambers of dogskull and jade.

I strung her teeth on living whipcords about my throat, skimmed her photophagous eyes across the glassy skin mosaics which paved the dunes; her ossified ovaries chattered like raving dice in my clutch. Carving down into her cloaca, I unpeeled the asphyxiated remnants of my idiot brother. The pale and melancholy disk of his face seemed holy, honeyed by a religious love for the tempest of razors at my core; lice teemed from his mouth, and in their abysmal chaos I saw the cartography of the void that beckoned me.

The shore convulsed, it seethed with a stencil of orgasmic starfish, the dreams of crustacea raping female meat; serrate obsidian threaded a catacomb of crawling carnage, an epiphany in pink pared down from the cathedral rack of spine-bones, fat-clotted barbs of hide and smoking visceral wreaths. Upon those innards the moon sloughed an engravure whose fireless scintilla revealed the gradations of a universe in which I was damned to ride a crucified mule foetus backwards through blood

FROM THE NOVELLA "WHITE SKULL"

curtains, baptised in the way of the raven sun; launched upon a coruscating trajectory which would cripple and toxify all in its span.

Constellations overlapped. The night tide kissed my ears with a carnal sussuration, the lisping of a goatskin cervix; averring the viscous, telling of tongues hilted in cosmic sphincters, titan labyrinths of gut in temples hewn from flaccid deepwater stone. I saw that the sea's velvet meniscus was a lens through which star-crawlers darkly viewed their oneiric analogues, a slender membrane shielding sleep from the assassins; ghost memories of fornication pressed mournful faces to its pane.

Exiled from this arena, I yet persisted as its murderous double. The vaults of my body, seeded from the beast whose signature was a falcate sperm in the slipstream, were gravid with a cult of scorpionic atavism first fomented in profane marine chambers, my pathology indelibly mirrored in the sidereal. Mine were the agonies of boiling blood, corpuscles loaded with vesuvial violence, the atom surge of testicular planets. Flesh did not become me. My accursed transit was shadowplay, a phosphorous afterburn glimpsed in the sockets of arachnid headbones; I thirsted.

A filthy spoke of vultures, buoyed on the sun's first gloating ribs, cast down its adumbration on the rocks and sylvan tracery beyond the beach; cowling the cacophonous spoor of my grave-black progenitor, the one whom men call *Murder*.

EAT/DRINK

Red roses, raw ramp, Satan dust on clit – bang, bang! zipper fox, I think I love you – peaches, plums, cherry pulp on nipples on soft white underbelly, cum on lips, on fangs, in slipstreams seeking cunt-heat.

Oh.

Excuse me. To begin at the end – at the climax – may seem impertinent. But life is laid in loops as well, we'll soon be there again, again to start again, the rise and fall of jetplanes. Tortured tin on tarmac? You might say that, the way my ribcage buckles under velvet hammers, the soft embrace of death machines. Black fur, black eyes, his pizzle skinned and glistening turns to marble, flecked and foaming in my throat.

I dreamt I ate a wolf.

Sun/moon. Pussycat zone: at tea with Alice O, her thighboots shiny face saliva-strung, cheek on vinyl, tongue in cunt, in asshole, cities burn in retinas. Telling me of soot-black sorrows, streets not paved with gold not paved at all.

Cut city. Pan to dirt-track. Girl with skirt raised pissing in a ditch, in lover's mouth. Stars. Stars blurry. Crystal nipples cold of cosmos, moonchild lip-twitch, hex express to the clear juice of mirror.

Candy calls; mirror shatters. I'd vowed to tattoo locusts on her white buttocks, snow everywhere, pulverised cables for an arctic ascension; angel frost on clit.

Dildos buckled, fingers greased, three girl six hole action.

FROM THE NOVEL "THE FEAST" BY JANA HEX

STEWART HOME

ORGASM ADDICT

NEW CALLGIRL SCANDAL?
Letters purporting to have proof of a call-girl ring involving certain government ministers and prominent MPs circulated Fleet Street yesterday.

Photostats have been given to Scotland Yard and some of those mentioned have already been interviewed. It is understood that all the men have strongly denied the allegations.

Post-marks show the letters came from every county in the South of England, most from the London area.

If the accusations are ever substantiated many familiar faces will be missing from televised political discussions.

MISS BEAUTIFUL KIDNAPPED
Within six hours of winning the 'Miss Beautiful' title, Maria Gomez from Mexico mysteriously vanished from her first-class London hotel.

Scotland Yard confirmed that a ransom demand has been discovered.

According to Luana Ferris of the Ferris Cosmetic Company which sponsors the contest the kidnappers have asked for £50,000 and a promise to bring 'this degrading competition' to an end.

Considering the number of Women's Lib supporters outside the Albert Hall during the televised finals it is speculated that the kidnapping is the work of a fringe section of the movement whose sole aim is the elimination of all beauty contests.

Every Monday afternoon Jimmy Crayson made six calls. Fourth on his list was Wilma the Witch. Entering Sloane Square he slipped a stick of chewing gum into his mouth, unconsciously brushed his hand across his hip pocket. He had a habit of doing this. And the feel of his cosh there invariably gave him a sense of security.

Approaching Wilma's flat he wondered how the hell her steady string of clients ever managed to find parking in the square. He'd never been able to spot a vacant space outside any of the houses or hotels. Thankfully he didn't have to drive around his district. The boss gave him a generous taxi allowance.

PREVIOUSLY UNPUBLISHED

When Wilma opened the door she wore make-up and a loose robe. Nothing else. Not even a pretence of modesty. 'You're early,' she said in a naturally husky voice, brushing auburn hair from her forehead.

There had been a time when Jimmy first started this job when he got hot under the belt seeing the girls in the nude. No longer. None of them had anything a million other pretty birds didn't possess. Oh, sure, some grouped it better and quite a few knew how to use it expertly – as compared to those fumbling, erratic efforts of the genuine amateur. But the bursting breasts, narrow waist and thick pubic hair didn't tempt him. Especially not today.

'You've been talking,' he told the woman.

Wilma's face tightened, spoiling her better-than-average looks.

'The boss has had a squeal from one of his newspaper mates...'

Going to a cupboard Wilma drew a bottle of Scotch from inside and held it aloft with a forced smile. 'The usual, Jimmy?'

'Why not!' he said, flopping on a divan. Eyes moving up and down, around and under her voluptuousness. Quite a crumpet. 'Sir Jarold Derrick didn't like his name linked to yours, Wilma. Fact, he was bleedin' wild!'

Wilma brought him a double, deliberately sensual as she snuggled against his thigh. 'I haven't the faintest what you're talking about.'

'Come off that shit,' the man said and sampled his drink. 'You know the score. All the other scandals blew up because some cheap tart got mouthy!'

'I swear, Jimmy...'

'I can swear, too,' he grinned. 'Man, did the boss ever swear. He called you some horrible bloody names!'

'Can I see him?'

'Naw – I'm to do the honours!'

'Jimmy – please.'

Finishing his drink Crayson pushed her off the divan. He liked the sound of her buttocks bouncing on the carpet. A sensual noise if a bloke were that way inclined. She lay sprawled with legs wide apart and kicking. Very arousing under other circumstances.

'I've always kicked back the full amount, Jimmy,' she said, gushing words in oil-rich eruption. 'I'd be cutting my own throat grassing on clients. Crissake, can't you see I'm no copper's nark!'

'I see something that isn't going to please Sir Jarold for the next few months,' Jimmy said softly, withdrawing his cosh and slapping it against an open palm. 'And when you recover, the word is find another flat. The boss needs this one for a replacement bit.'

Fear contorted Wilma's features.

'Ready, sweetheart?' The cosh made another circuit – sliced air close to her kneecap.

'Jimmy... I'll give you the best screw you've ever had!'

The cosh whistled, landed across her cheekbone. Before the cracking reached his ears, Jimmy had a new target in aim. Slowly, professionally, he used the small deadly weapon until Wilma lay unconscious on the floor. Blood pouring from a dozen different wounds. Face a pulped mess. Breasts and thighs marked, bruised. Arms limp and twisted at crazy angles.

Going to the drinks cupboard the man helped himself to another double. Removed an envelope containing the boss's percentage of her take, stuck it in his pocket and – as a grinning afterthought – wiped the blood from his cosh on the woman's buttocks.

Whistling now, he left the flat. Briefly touched his hip pocket for reassurance. Nodded to an elderly lady opening her flat door. Just another youngish man going about his 'ordinary' business. A collector and regulator...

A wave of kidnappings gave Fleet Street headaches trying to decide which victim rated the largest headline. One 'normal' bank raid where five hostages were taken to guarantee the robbers' safety was given only a small insertion on the inside pages.

Charles Killiger, the American playboy diplomat, hit the fancy of three editorial eye-assaults. Kidnapped in Paris.

In Mexico City, spinster-columnist Hedy Harper vanished from her 'virgin' bed as her latest attack on the Libber hierarchy went on the syndicated rounds in the US.

In Sydney, Australia, a bizarre abduction caught the attentions of Aussie readers. Panjit Bannerjee's whisking away from the scene of a world population conference had its comic side. Blamed for not easing the lot of Hindu women, the ransom demand was for a United Nations team of doctors and at least five million proven sterilisation operations on Indian males.

In Athens a narrow escape for Miklos Kraikadolinis. His leap from a second floor bedroom in the nude resulted in several broken bones and amnesia – and a temporary end to a Greek shipping magnate's on-board seduction of a string of beautiful global models.

In Vancouver, Canada, a trade commissioner home on leave from Britain is another victim. The price for his release is his replacement by his female secretary and an amount equivalent to the market value of his Belgrave Square property.

WOMEN USE BODIES TO GAIN THEIR ENDS

one tongue-in-cheek editorial writer used as his leader head.

Everybody had the notion now – the kidnappings were definitely the work of a fanatical Libber movement.

But while he still believed that Libbers were behind the kidnappings, Bill White had reached a new conclusion. Women, in his eyes, could entice men to drop their guards – and trousers. But it took more than a sexy smile and a baring of bosoms to get an able-bodied man into a hijack vehicle. It took some force – and he didn't reckon women had yet reached the kung-fu expertise to rampage round the globe. Not on this scale. And not with the kind of military organisation timetable the reports seemed to suggest.

A note from Lionel Blane landed on Inspector Doland's desk. Reprinted in full in *The Globe-Mercury*...

Do what they say. My life is in danger. I am well but delay could change conditions.

Doland frowned and accepted the note back. Our handwriting experts confirm it's legitimate,' he said through a fog of cigar smoke. White flicked a cigarette into his mouth, pondering if he'd have been better off using a Tic-Tac; *Why flick a weed when you can flick two mints!*

'I don't like it, Bill – I sure as hell don't.'

'You've got something you haven't told me?'

Doland took a nail file from his pocket and carefully evened off a ragged index fingernail. 'Only my personal opinion of Blane,' he growled as he worked. 'He's like a once lovely garden gone to weed!'

Bill White wondered why he had never said that in good old 'journalese'!

Replacing the file the inspector sat back and gazed at his cigar-stained ceiling. He could see now why his wife objected to too much smoking in the home. She claimed it coated mirrors and windows and gave curtains a stale smell. A reason for having as many windows as possible open summer and winter.

'Do you figure Blane is in danger?'

Doland grunted, brought his attention back on the reporter. He liked Bill. More than he cared to admit in an official capacity. They'd grown apart during the past years but the old feelings were still a bond he respected. 'Only if he asks for a queer to sleep the night with him!'

Bill grinned. This was his mate! The down to earth sergeant whose honesty had shaken a few Soho porn kings out of their specially woven socks. 'What didn't you like, then?'

'The whole damned set-up... and that's what it is! We're being conned. I'd lay odds not one kidnap victim is harmed even if the demands are refused.'

'Not if the show is being run by Women's Lib,' Bill said softly.

'Which means?'

'There could be others involved. Bright boys cashing in on the action!'

'And they'd play rough?'

'Once the notion of profit gets hold it's tough to let a soft touch go!'

Doland leapt to his feet, scowling. 'If it was just in London I'd agree – but, dammit, this is worldwide! The heavies don't cooperate that far afield.'

'Student dissidents do.'

'Bloody hell!' Doland slumped back in his creaking chair. 'If we're up against amateurs...'

'We're up a creek without a proverbial paddle,' Bill finished.

'What gave you the idea?'

Lighting another cigarette as he stubbed the first out, White coughed once – deep-down and soft – the worst kind, he'd been warned. 'Hunch, Tommy,' he said. 'Working on the theory that Libbers tend to be intellectuals and snobs into the bargain. Bra dropouts in a sense...' He laughed, liked the sentence.

'Right out of university,' Doland said, not catching the drop-out bit. 'Rebels with plenty of contacts. Yes, I like the connection. It's logical.'

'And those jokers always want bread,' Bill remarked, hand up. 'Please don't give me the fuzz verdict for grass and booze. It's not always true. Some of them are struggling to complete their education. Others in providing for a wife and kids – they get married on grants nowadays, you know.'

Doland returned the hand up gesture. 'No need to convince me, Bill – I've got kids, remember? One's at Keele. I have managed to gasp the "drift".'

White shrugged. 'It is feasible, though!'

'Very,' the Inspector allowed generously. 'I'll have the idea spread.'

'And I'll do my own breeding,' Bill remarked. 'Germs planted where they'll find incubator conditions.'

Doland lifted his eyes to the ceiling again. 'With that – get lost, mate.'

Bill nodded, left a butt smoking in the desk ashtray. He couldn't think of a more appropriate exit.

Carnaby Street has been a tourist Mecca for several decades and while the fashions displayed in the shop windows constantly change, there are plenty of specialist outlets catering to those with a nostalgic bent. I'd been invited to a sixties party and wanted to gear up as a mod. It was a Monday morning and the only sign of excitement in the premises I'd entered was the sound of a Desmond Dekker greatest hits CD booming out from Wharfdale speakers.

'Can I help you?' a woman in her late thirties enquired.

'Yeah, I want a suit,' I replied.

'What size?'

'Thirty-six inch chest, thirty waist, thirty-one leg, charcoal grey.'

I didn't need to state the style, the only type sold in the shop were the three button affairs with narrow lapels that had been favoured by mods during the cult's sixties heyday. The sales assistant pulled what I needed from a rack and handed it to me as I stepped into the store's only changing cubical. I took off my coat and then dropped my trousers.

'How's it going?' the woman asked as she yanked back the curtain.

'I haven't got the damn thing on yet!' I replied as I stepped into a freshly ironed pair of sta-prest trousers.

The shop assistant zipped up the fly as I fastened the button on the waist-band. The woman smiled at me, the corners of her mouth turned up in a laugh as she took in my mild embarrassment. I slipped on the jacket and the sales girl ran her hands over my body, simultaneously smoothing down the odd crease in the material.

'All the boys look very smart in our clothes,' the woman told me. Then touching my erection with her hand added, 'the tight fit shows your body to its full advantage.'

I tried to put my arms around the sales girl but she stepped out of the cubical. Reaching forward again, she grabbed my shoulders and then spun me around, so that I was looking at myself in a full length mirror.

'Being dressed in a smart suit must make you feel more of a man!' the shop assistant cried.

'Yeah, I feel really good,' I crowed as I looked at myself in the mirror. 'But why don't you wear the kind of clothes that are sold in here, I like what you've got on but it would be great to see you in mod girl gear.'

'No, no, no!' the woman shot back, 'I'm not a youngster like you, it wouldn't be dignified at my age, I'm more at home wearing skirts from Marks and Sparks.'

'You're not that much older than me!' I protested. 'And I'm sure if you let your hair down, you'd be asked for proof of your age every time you tried to order a drink in a pub.'

The shop assistant fiddled with some clips and then shook her head, so that her shiny black hair cascaded around her shoulders. With her face framed in this fashion, the woman's infectious smile was even more stunning than the first time I'd clocked it.

'I think that dark suit is a little too sombre for you,' the sales girl observed gravely. 'What about trying one in a different colour?'

'Blue,' I said, 'let's see what I look like in blue.'

As I hung up the first suit I'd tried, the woman zipped around the shop. I smiled as she locked the door. Split-seconds later, she was back with me, a new suit, white socks, black tie, white shirt, union jack boxer shorts and loafer shoes in her hands.

'I want you nicely packaged,' the shop assistant told me, 'your grey briefs and socks are a fashion mistake. The loafers are size nine, you'll look a lot better in them than those awful trainers.'

I stripped off. Once I was naked, the sales girl stroked my pubic hair but was very careful to avoid touching my throbbing erection. She handed me the union jack boxer shorts and I stepped into them. Then I pulled on the socks and slipped into the shirt. The woman lifted my collar and wrapped the tie around my neck, knotting it and pulling it tight. After this, I slipped into the sta-prest trousers, jacket and shoes. Once again, the shop assistant smoothed down the creases in my clothes. This time she kissed me on the cheek before stepping back to admire my sartorial elegance.

'You look great!' the woman said admiringly, 'I told you all the boys look very smart in our clobber!'

I spread my arms and stepped towards the sales girl but once again she spun me around. I gazed at my reflection in the mirror and what I saw did a great deal to add to my self-confidence. It made me wonder why I'd spent so much of my life slouching around in jeans and a leather jacket. Power is sexy and the mod gear gave me an aura of youth and vitality, something that is often in short supply among men in their late twenties.

This time as I advanced on the woman, she let me put my arms around her. We kissed but she pulled back as I tried to force my tongue into her mouth.

'You're too greedy for it,' the sales girl laughed. 'I like to take things slowly, I want you to smell my hair and then kiss it.'

I took the shop assistant in my arms a second time and pressed my nose against the crown of her head. I sniffed and inhaled a peachy fragrance. Her hair smelt really fresh, I guess she must have washed it that morning. I let two great handfuls of the woman's silky black hair slip through my fingers as I kissed the top of her head. Then I moved my mouth to the right until I was kissing and eventually nibbling at the sales girl's ear.

'That's really nice,' the woman laughed as I bit her lobe, 'but now I want you to start at the other end of my body, I want you to give me a shrimp job.'

'Okay,' I agreed, 'but I'd better take off my trousers because I don't want to crease them.'

As I kicked off my loafers, the shop assistant stepped out of her white stilettos. While I carefully folded the sta-prest, she peeled off her tights. The sales girl sat on a high stool that had been placed by the till. I got on my knees and licked at the purple varnish that had been painted over her toe nails. Then, I worked my tongue in and out of the cracks between her toes. While I was doing this, a youth banged on the door.

'Come back in twenty minutes,' the woman shouted at him, 'the shop is closed right now.'

I took the sales girl's big toe in my mouth and sucked on it. She moved her foot back and forth, I quickly caught on to what she wanted and bobbed my head up and down, so that my lips were rolling up and down the toe.

'That feels so nice,' the shop assistant moaned, 'it's got me all wet! Now I want you to run your tongue around my clit!'

The woman stood up, simultaneously rolling her skirt around her waist. I raised my head and pressed my mouth against her pubic thatch. I flicked my tongue back and forth across her clitoris, then ran my nose up and down her slit. Her olive brown skin beautifully offset a profuse tangle of jet black hair.

'Work your tongue up my hole!' the sales girl screamed as I lapped at her quim.

I did as I was told, then replaced the tongue with a finger and successfully penetrated the site of her mystery. I worked a second digit into the shop assistant's cunt, while simultaneously using my mouth to lap at her clitoris. Sex juice was splashing between the woman's legs and she was bellowing the sweetest of obscenities.

'You beautiful bastard!' the sales girl howled as I worked her hole with my fingers and mouth. 'That feels so good! Now I want you to lie on your back!'

The woman hauled the boxer shorts I was wearing over my ankles and then rolled a condom down my prick. With my cock in her hand, she straddled my thighs and guided the throbbing member into her cunt.

'Lie still, I'm setting the pace!' the shop assistant barked as I thrust upwards.

Allowing my buttocks to sink back against the floor, I obeyed. Ever so slowly, the woman raised and lowered her body. These movements became more and more subtle, until she was sitting motionless above me.

'Can you feel my cunt muscles contracting?' my partner demanded. 'Do you like it?'

'Yes, yes!' I yelled. 'Your body fits me like a glove!'

'I've studied tantric sex and I'm gonna make you come by relaxing and then increasing the grip I've got on your prick!' the woman hissed.

I could feel the muscles in my crotch contracting as she worked me up towards orgasm. The sales girl's hands were pressed against my chest and I grabbed her tits before shooting off a great wad of liquid genetics. The shop assistant yelped with pleasure as a simultaneous orgasm swept through our twin bulks. Then she tilted forward and fell panting against me.

The few minutes during which we lay together on the carpet were an utterly blissful moment of union. Then the sales girl got up, pulled on her knickers and unlocked the door. I skulked back into the fitting room split-seconds before a customer came through the door. Once I was dressed, I paid for the blue suit with a credit card.

'I can't remember how much those ties cost,' the woman laughed, 'so I haven't put it on the bill. I hope you're honest enough to come back in a few days to settle up the difference.'

'Oh yes,' I assured her, 'I'll be back!'

Even naked, Luana Ferris was far from being just another woman. Aware of her beauty, her marvellously voluptuous figure, she radiated a certain elegant charm that set her apart from the pin-up creation.

Letting his pyjama bottoms drop, White could not help but enthuse over her stark loveliness. Those schoolgirls had not been wrong, either. She deserved the nickname 'Bushy', the unashamed glory that rightly captivated. 'I don't give a damn what a man's looking for in a bedmate, but you...' He sucked air into his lungs.

'Like?' Luana asked, almost virginally.

'Adore!'

'I'm always worried...'

'See your psychiatrist!'

Her head momentarily drooped, eyes fastening on the thick pubic curls. Raven-black as her head.

'Even the tit-and-bum merchants would have to consult a thesaurus to find enough words in praise of that!'

'You make it sound so... well, crude!'

'Far from it, Luana. Come here...'

As she moved into his waiting arms the scent of delicate perfume rose from between her breasts. All pretensions were now flying as the sensations of flesh on flesh shattered miscellaneous thoughts until there was but one mutual yearning.

'The bed's in there,' Bill grunted; hand on her buttock, fingers squeezing.

'Gently, I don't want to be bruised!' She moved with him through the doorway, fascinated by the muscles rippling under his now glistening skin.

He lay on the bed, on his spine. Reached out to draw her down beside him. Watching the way her breasts swung outwards as she bent forward; a pair of ripe fruits suspended above Eden's fertile garden.

'Oh, God...' He rolled with her, their lengths pressing hotly. His mouth

PREVIOUSLY UNPUBLISHED

sought hers and they kissed. Deeply. And all the while his hands roamed her back – from shoulders to bottom, separating to cup each full buttock. The heat of her breasts flattening on his chest aroused him enormously. Her fingernails, working along his upper torso like crawling spiders, were extra-sensitive incitements.

Pulling her mouth from his she sucked in air, body moving to assume a superior position.

'No! Take hold of me!'

Immediately her hand encircled him, White brought them into their sides. Found a breast, letting the nipple stiffen under his tweaking.

She panted aloud, small beads of perspiration forming on her upper lip. Eyes closed, she gave herself wholly to contact stimulation.

His hand slid down her flesh, between her damp thighs. Automatically, more a result of her own raging passion than any desire to please him, her thighs parted. Gasping, his fingers dug into the softly tender inner surfaces. His mouth finding and closing on her swollen breast.

'Bill... Bill...' she moaned over and over again, surrendering entirely to that insidious hand. To the way he fingered her. To the unbearable torment seething within willing loins.

'Ready?'

Something snapped inside her!

Tearing from his grasp she jumped off the bed, breasts heaving. Body coated with lust's film. Stomach muscles dancing beneath the flesh.

'What the blazes?' He stared at her without understanding.

'Wait... I won't be long! I've got to get something for you...' She swung, buttocks bouncing firmly.

'Christ, don't you take the bloody Pill?'

She was halfway across the living room, making for her purse. 'No,' she shouted, voice edged and deep.

Impatience boiled inside him. *What a damned carry-on!* If only she had mentioned this earlier – he kept a few sheaths in his medicine cabinet. Left-overs from 'ancient' days, and nights.

She came through the door, flushed. Eyes fixing on his pride with shadowed curiosity. Hand behind her back like a naughty child caught stealing biscuits from a kitchen jar.

'Get back down here!' White grunted.

Smiling now, Luana climbed on to the bed – doing everything possible to keep him inflamed. Letting his hand instantly return to its former cajoling position between her parted thighs. Breasts swinging teasingly over his face. 'A few minutes and I'll put it on,' she murmured sexily.

'No time to waste,' he growled, face buried into her perfumed orbs. 'Do it now!'

She brought her hand from behind her, moved it up... a breast shifting from his searching mouth.

More in surprise than awareness he moved his head to see what she intended doing and caught the glint of a hypodermic needle point coming to zero in on his shoulder. Thrusting at her weight he managed to seize her wrist, the sharp needle less than an inch from breaking his skin. Sweat poured from his forehead. He strained, forced her back... back...

'Bastard!' she raged.

Wrenching the hypodermic from her he whooshed air from his lungs, sat on his bottom and stared into her contorted face. 'You rotten bitch! You conniving tart! I don't bloody mind being suckered, but not when you blasted well are panting to be screwed! That's the giddy limit!'

Luana relaxed, all hate oozing from her pores. Her flesh crawled to be satisfied. Inside, the furies raged – begging for gratification.

'Why?' White asked, examining the hypo. Finding the liquid level to the top. A single drip showing how she'd primed it in preparation.

'You're menacing us,' Luana said lifelessly.

'Us?'

'That's all I'm going to say,' she replied, eyes closing to avoid the sight of his nudity. She still wanted him.

'You'll talk, Miss Ferris,' the man grated. 'You'll bloody talk – and this will do the trick!' He squirted fluid across her breasts, brought the needle down towards her.

Her eyes opened, saw the danger. 'No! Don't – please!'

Bill laughed bitterly. 'What's good for the goose, and all that crap!' The point almost touched her upper arm.

'I'll tell you...'

Conscious of her naked beauty and eager to continue where they left off, White positioned her so that he could threaten with the hypodermic held in one hand whilst keeping her aroused with the other. 'As for you,' he said tightly, 'you could play around *as* you talk!'

Luana trembled, reached out for him. The needle holding her mesmerised.

'First,' Bill asked, 'are you on the Pill?'

'Of course!'

'When we've got the story out of you...'

She shook all over, passion starting to rampage anew.

'Now...' He steadied himself, shutting off that portion of his mind dwelling on the excitements of what his fingers were doing to her. 'Let's hear about these phoney kidnappings. Start with Maria Gomez...'

'She's safe. Unharmed.'

'I know that – how did you get her out of the hotel?'

'She walked out with me.' Luana smiled, then as a new wave washed up from her loins, groaned. 'It's hard to...'

'Yeah, I know!' Bill replied provocatively.

For once, Luana Ferris had to play the underdog. She detested his ability to separate emotions from his chosen profession of snoop.

'None of the hotel staff saw her leave.'

'She wore a man's suit, had her hair brushed up inside a hat. It was made to look like she belonged to my party. In the crush and packed lobby nobody noticed anything unusual.'

'Where is she?'

'With friends. She stays indoors but isn't a prisoner.'

'And Lionel Blane?'

'In a different location. He has whatever he wants except freedom to come and go.'

Keeping the hypo ready to stab, Bill bent over her and kissed her mouth. Her arms started to raise. He withdrew. 'Better not,' he scowled. 'There's more to spill!'

Luana lay supine, an object for use.

'What's behind this?' White asked, puzzled still by the mathematics of the campaign. 'It doesn't fit. You kidnap Maria and the demand is for all beauty contests by your company to end. That doesn't make any sense.'

'I'd like a drink,' Luana said, pleading eyes fixed on his.

'Ah, hell!' He got to his feet, slowly withdrawing his hand from between her thighs. Subtle sounds tricking his ears, driving him into a controlled rage. 'Outside!' he ordered. 'And don't give me trouble or I'll bruise you like a battered tomato.'

She swung her legs off the bed, saw how damp she was. Murmured, 'If only, Bill.'

'I know! I bloody know!' He pushed her through the doorway when she stood, leaving the hypodermic syringe on a bedside table as he followed. The door was locked to the outside world. And if he couldn't handle one woman he didn't deserve to be called a man. But to make sure she had no other cute traps in her purse he opened it and examined the contents. The usual female junk, he concluded. Cosmetics – all Ferris expensive. Comb and handkerchief. Tissues – for what? Loose change. Seven ten pound notes. Two credit cards and an 'in case of accident notify' emergency address.

'Satisfied?' Luana asked, poised again. Standing nearby, with her nudity now a thing of slight embarrassment but not a deterrent.

'Sit down where I can watch you!'

'Kinky?'

'Yeah – like screw crazy!' He got their glasses and poured fresh drinks.

Lit a cigarette and self-consciously held his ambered glass in a provocative toast to the gods.

Luana Ferris smiled grimly. 'It doesn't hide all,' she remarked acidly.

'No more, I suppose, than it could hide your contender for global honours,' he retorted nastily. Gave her the glass and retreated to the chair opposite. Sat and crossed his legs. Felt able now to handle her – mentally. Knew the physical handling was 'on' when they finished talking.

'I almost had you,' Luana said.

'In two ways!'

She inclined her head as an admission of fact.

'Let's get back to why Maria was kidnapped,' he said. 'How did you expect to cash in?'

The woman regarded her drink, slowly sipped. 'Strong,' she told him.

'Get on with the story – I'm not catering for any more of your demands!'

'All right...' She duplicated his modesty and crossed her legs. Not quite achieving the result she wanted. Providing him with an anxious moment of some revealing titillation. 'You've a dirty mind!'

'Not dirty, luv – normal!' He flicked ash into a nearby container. Waved for her to continue. Enjoying his stiff drink.

'I'm one of many women who believe that men have dominated for too many centuries,' Luana began, eyes glittering. Fanatically. 'Women can meet men on a level in every field, as I've successfully proved. We're not just receptacles for sperm. Not just housewives and bearers of unlimited brats. We're indispensable beings. Without us the cycle would cease. We have rights – equal pay, equal pensions, equality in housing and mortgages, in the purchase of credit goods. Of being heads of State. About a year ago some of us got together...'

Bill White made mental notes. This was the meat Frank Worthington wanted for *Post Intelligencer*.

Luana sipped from her glass. Conscious of his undivided attention. Knowing that her body no longer held major sway. Thankful for the central heating which kept his flat at a non-goosepimpling temperature.

'We had women from several countries present. All agreed there should be a concerted effort made to bring the plight of females before the general public through newspapers. After some hours we arrived at a plan. One involving me intimately. One which would seem to eliminate me from any enquiry should events get out of hand. Although my company has sponsored beauty contests for many years I am not in favour of girls parading around like a bunch of eager whores offering their bodies for a shot at fame and minimal fortune. I was prepared to let Ferris Cosmetics write-off a tax deductible amount in order to gain global publicity for Woman's Lib. More, I agreed to drop all further contests – knowing this would increase my sales by five hundred per cent... the computer said so!'

Bill finished his cigarette and lit another. He looked at their glasses, saw no desperate need to replenish either. Let Luana get it off her enviable chest.

'Our idea was to grab headlines,' the woman said, not in the least interested now in what the man did or how he reacted. 'From the ransom demands we anticipated funds coming into an international kitty. This, we assumed, would pay for greedy male politicians who had community standing. Men able to rush laws through their various parliaments – granting woman rights they had not held previously. The kidnapping of Lionel Blane was aimed at shaming the homosexual clique. Making them appear as ineffectual as they are in reality...'

'I can't quite gasp that, Luana,' White said, interjecting. 'You girls are bent on making us subservient to your demands yet you deny...'

Luana finished her drink and coughed delicately. 'Too strong – make this one weaker!' She extended her arm, glass catching the light. 'We're not against having sex with men. All of us at that conference enjoyed intercourse. And not a lesbian in sight.'

Bill got to his feet, let her admire what had to be a major attraction soon. Downed his Scotch and went to do his duty in a non-bed sense. A good host always liquored up his bird before he... A smile wreathed his face. He had almost thought 'licked her up'... There, he had!

'Can't you see that Blane is a symbol?' Luana asked.

Pouring, Bill nodded. A splash of soda settled on his belly sending shivers down him.

'If we rid the parliamentary scene of those most concerned with male dominance we gain a moral victory,' the woman claimed.

'And what about the blokes you've got helping you?'

Luana Ferris assumed a company executive posture, took her drink with a curt silent movement of lips. 'There are some things women cannot do,' she announced. 'We didn't want paid criminals nor would we tolerate anyone but those in need as we were. We decided that some student dissidents qualified for a hand-out. We made a deal with one group. A percentage of ransom for their help.'

'What group?' Bill asked, worried.

'Is that important?'

'To me – yes!'

'They call themselves "Students for Democratic Equality".'

Bill shuddered mentally. 'I've heard about them – thugs whose aim is to create global anarchy. The establishment of a no-law, no-restriction permissive society with all those against eliminated. Not what I'd call decent bedfellows.'

'A typical male dominant reaction,' Luana shouted.

'Yeah?' Bill grinned. 'Ask yourself this question – would you birds have the strength to combat hellbent idealists whose only social responsibility was to grab every hand-out the State could offer and whose sole aim was the subjugation of women? Think about it, Luana. Think hard and long.'

'If you are right...'

White delved deep into his memory. 'Example,' he finally quoted. 'A campus riot in the Mid-West of America. "Students for Democratic Equality" ring-leaders. When the main university building was taken over every girl student was raped, forced to perform perversions to satisfy the leadership they were in agreement with the ideals of the rebellion.'

'I don't know...' Luana whispered.

'Example,' Bill continued, in full flight now. 'Six student members of this thug-band attended a demonstration in London recently. They stomped a policeman into hospital for nearly three months and rampaged through an Embassy – raping four secretaries in the process.'

'We've been wrong, Bill...'

'Bloody right you have!'

'How can we...?' She sounded distraught.

Bill grinned. 'Look, Luana – release all your victims. Send the word out – and I guarantee if *every* prisoner is freed I won't print a single word of this. I'll have my editor confirm – in writing – that we will sponsor a Lib programme aimed at equal rights in every sphere. How's that?'

Luana laughed, relieved. 'I think it's terrific!'

'I think you're terrific,' he said, eyes again passionately fixed on her firm breasts.

'Really?' She uncrossed her legs.

'God – do you have to show it all at once?'

Luana Ferris got to her feet. All frontally exposed. 'Mind if I freshen my make-up?'

'If it makes you congenial...'

'You had me worried,' Luana laughed, going to her purse. 'I thought you were about to say genital!'

'That remark calls for one last drink.'

'Like we need it?' Her violet eyes had a target.

From *The Globe-Mercury*, August 29...

THE PRICE OF BEAUTY

Luana Ferris of Ferris Cosmetics announced today that her company had paid the £50,000 to secure the release of newly crowned Miss Beautiful, Maria Gomez from Mexico. Included in the deal was a promise that Ferris would no longer hold its annual contest which has become an established tradition in the world's 'flesh on parade' hate target for Women's Libbers. Miss Gomez, in a brief interview after she was safely returned to the Ferris tower-block headquarters, said: 'I was treated civilly. My captors were men – and they spoke about their aims. They did not believe the money was important. Only that women should not be put on display like cattle in a market.'

CLINT HUTZULAK

She says: it is afternoon; you are still at the table. On a plate, the crust from a sandwich she made is drying. The air thickens and darkens between you. Cups. saucers, hands, become blurred and forgotten in the dusk. Nothing moves in the room, only your voice. Outside the house, crickets raise a fine mist of noise from the grass.

She says: in the mind of the woman is a flutter as if of wings. Then there is a long silence.

One. You are standing in a tunnel of leaves. A wasp circles your leg in meaningful unimportant patterns. When you open your mouth a fist of cool air slides into your throat. The must of decay, the blackened leaves going back to earth in lank dry grass. Look up through the pleached branches. It is late afternoon, the light is evaporating. The faint trail fading under your feet. You are going deeper. Bracken ferns, bleached by frost, the tiny golden leaves of the saskatoons bobbing like lost coins.

Two. You know how it ends, but not how to get there.

Three. You have made up your mind. The woman leads you further. Behind, everything is erased. Ahead, you see only the woman's shirt. You have no part of the past, no part of a future. Your head is rushing like a clock, counting backward to some invisible room in the middle of your chest, the length of the trail spooling out crazily like the length of a whole poisoned life as you follow the woman through the trees. She is leading you to the trailer. This is where you will sleep. At the table you made up your mind. The suitcase bucking against your knee as you carry everything with you, away from the house.

Four. She says you look tired, as if you had not slept in a year. You nod. Doors are opening everywhere, there is an electric hum in the house, she has turned on the television though you have not seen her leave the room. The man is in the hallway unscrewing the light bulbs. As he stretches up soft rotten gas eases out from his asshole. Everything is rotten and confused. The last pane of glass topples out slowly from the window frame where you imagine you have put your fist. You stop your head just before it hits the tabletop. I want to sleep, you say, but

I cannot sleep in this house.

Five. Together you go out of the house, her hand on your arm now. It is the not the first time she has touched you. A broken handle of a rake in the grass, a shaky pile of oil filters on a black circle of gravel, the clouds shining like beaten silver from below, the light reflected up from the great swath of prairie. She has switched on the pole lamp, and it hangs above the yard like a pale medallion against the sullen sky.

Six. Only half will be recorded here.

Seven. She leads you to the trailer. An orange tarpaulin has been stretched over the entire trailer and lashed with rotting string to bumper, hitch, grommets, the flaking electroplated handle on the door. Where the tarp has lain over the edges of the trailer roof black mildew is growing. She unties the string on the door, opens the trailer. The house is hidden from you by the long screen of trees which have been left to grow along the fence. You can sleep out here until we figure out what to do, she says. When Theobald comes back we can decide how we're going to sort everything out. You touch the side of the woman's neck. She shakes her head, then suddenly she turns to you and lays her head against your shoulder. Perhaps it is all a mystery. The confused instinct of limbs, corroded wires in your head and chest, you are touching her now as if you knew what you were doing. You go inside the trailer. Through the door you see the naked man standing within the tunnel of trees, watching you.

Eight. The real story. You will not find it here.

Nine. When ten is reached, you will realize there is no option but to continue.

I've hidden it here, she says. The telltale heart. Beneath these ribs. She puts her hand where her heart should be.

He pulls her toward him. The floor shifts beneath them as they sit together on the edge of the mattress.

It's not very stable, she says. You'll have to prop it up with cinder blocks. The ground is soft here.

The lumpy mattress is thin and greening with mildew. He tests it with the palm of his hand, then leans back on one elbow, resting his head awkwardly against the wall of the trailer. She remains sitting on the edge of the bunk, her hands together between her knees.

Tell me about your heart, he says.

She shakes her head. Sometimes I don't think there's much left. There's not a lot to say.

Most of the time I feel nothing. Then something makes me think of you – maybe a dream, or the print of a brat heel in the dirt, a radio playing – and even then it's not really a pain I feel but there is a trace, you know, even after so long. A little hitch, and I would know you were still out there, though a long way off, and the line was still connecting you and me. It's like a fish hooked deep inside, waiting down at the bottom of the lake, too hurt to move, just floating there still and waiting with the hook in its guts, sending the tiniest tremors up the line.

I'm sorry if you were hurt, he says.

Every time you touch me, you leave a scar, Jezebel Rae says. She pulls the bottom of her shirt from her jeans, twisting sideways to display a fading pucker of scar at the base of her spine. Remember when I got this one, she asks. No. Monster does not remember. He puts his fingers on her skin, feels the velvet knot of vertebrae. He moves his hand up her body, until he is under her shirt. Jezebel Rae says nothing. Awkwardly, he unfastens the small clasp of her bra.

What do you think, he asks. He kisses her arm. The smell of clean cotton.

She leans forward, rests her elbow on her knees. With one hand she loosens a plait of hair, shaking it out across her shoulders. I got that scar when I was a kid, she says. We were cleaning trout by the lake. You always said you liked the smell of fresh trout – the guts smelled sweet to you when you opened them up. We were kneeling down together in the shade of the boathouse. It must have been early summer, because the trailer for the motorboat was right there, behind us, and when I stood up the corner of the license plate on the trailer got me right on the spine. You said you could see white gristle it cut so deep.

Monster runs his fingertips over the ridge of skin. Why didn't you get stitches?

Jezebel Rae shakes her head. Too dangerous. Anaesthetic on the spine can paralyze you.

Monster slides his hand down the back of her jeans until the nub of her coccyx is under his fingers. Do you have other scars, he asks. He reaches under her arm, opens the top of her jeans.

Most of the scars are inside, she says. The scars are mine, not yours. Only I can read them. The one on the inside of my elbow is from the time we were making love in the back of your car, when my arm got stuck in the crack between the seats. Do you remember that?

No. Monster does not remember.

It is as if you are a perfect stranger, she says. She pulls his head down and kisses him, twice, on the eyes.

He pulls her back down against him so that she is laying across his chest, puts his mouth to the side of her throat.

The faint smell of talcum on her skin. He runs his fingers through her hair, spreading it out strand by strand in a black net over her face until she brushes it aside and brings his mouth down to hers, pushing her tongue into his startled mouth. They kiss slowly, feeding on the movement of lips which seem to know exactly the patterns of pleasure. Blood tugging at the base of his cock. He presses against her hip, lifts a thigh up and over her, feeling his erection slide across the fly of her jeans.

She unbuttons her shirt, letting it fall back away from her body onto the bed. Her shoulders tense against the mattress.

It's been a long time since I've been touched the way you are touching me now, she says.

He loosens her bra, pushes it back off her shoulders, moves his hand down across her breasts, stops at her belly. Her breasts elastic and warm under his mouth.

Your hands are trembling, she says.

She traps his hand there, stroking with the ball of her thumb the back of his hand.

Nothing that is left here belongs to you, she says. It is as if you are a perfect stranger.

I am a stranger, Monster says. You've got it all wrong. What you think you know of me is all wrong. I've come to you but I have not come back. He kisses the soft hollow at the base of her throat, where a vein pulses, letting his tongue trace small intimate patterns on skin.

This morning I woke up and in my head you were already there. I must have been dreaming about you, because your ring was on my finger. Maybe I had put it on before I went to bed; maybe I put it on in the night in my sleep. Somehow knowing. She closes her eyes, pushes his fingers down her body.

They listen to the tick of a watch on the floor by the bed.

I think you should light the stove, she says. She rolls off the bed, stepping out of her jeans, which she kicks toward the door. Lets her shirt fall on the floor. Her legs white as clay as they go into dark work socks. Are you going to undress, she asks.

No.

He turns over to look up at her. She leans against the aluminum coaming of the countertop, tilting her head back to rest on a broken cabinet door. Stares up at the curved roof. He uses this trailer in the summer, she says. It's like a playpen for him. Nights he's off the road he comes out here to play cards with Archie. I don't allow them in the house when they're at cards. Sometimes they're out here till four, five in the morning. Sometimes Archie brings a girlfriend, maybe two, along, and then god knows what goes on. She pushes a tin lid full of cigarette butts across the top of the counter until with a clatter the lid falls into the sink. They don't have to worry about mosquitoes, there's so much smoke. One time Archie tried to come in the house. Maybe he didn't even know he was in our house. He came into the house, into my room, while Theobald was passed out under the card table out here. Drunk. I was sound asleep and when I woke up the sweating pig was knocking the alarm clock off the night table by my bed. Drunk. He wanted to fuck. He must have known where he was. I left him laying where he fell across the bed and went out to sleep in the truck with the doors locked.

I'm sorry, he says.

What are you sorry about, she says. She puts an arm across her belly, protectively.

Sit down here, he says, moving his legs on the bed. You must be getting cold.

I can't believe I'm standing here with no clothes on, she says, sitting on the bed. I want you to make love to me right now, before I change my mind.

The deep rift of her spine, arched under his hand. He rolls out from beneath her, kneeling on the floor of the trailer, shifts her so that her legs are one on each side of him. The soft inside of her thighs flaring slightly where they lay over the edge of the bunk.

You bastard, she says. She pulls his mouth into her, tilting her pelvis up hungry for his touch, the smell of her through cotton worn so thin he can see the swell and cleft of her pudendum. He puts his mouth to her, breathing through thin fabric until it is damp and clinging with his breath. Her hands like wires holding him there, his head. He kisses the soft fleshy inside of her thighs, letting his tongue slip under the elastic of her underwear now, and she drags the underwear down, parts her glistening pussy with a finger. He bites gently at her hand, pushes the tip of his tongue past her knuckle and into her wetness. At first there is the bitter tang of urea and then he is lapping quickly at her, her cunt suddenly running silk, his cock jammed against the edge of the bed through his jeans. The muscles inside his mouth strain to reach deeper, to reach the long channel inside her, but from the angle he is at it is impossible to penetrate more deeply. He kisses her, rolling the soft lip off flesh back into his mouth as he sucks at her clitoris, feeling his face wet and slick against the cool shuddering thigh. Jesus christ, jesus christ, her breathing sharp and frantic in the small bunk. He curves his mouth to her as if he will consume her very flesh, swallowing the liquid running down to her ass, pushing his finger into the tight whorled bud of her anus, reaming her out until she lifts her ass off the bed with two fists under her buttocks, her thighs across his shoulders.

It's like a secret language, she pants.

She works her fingers into his hair, pulling him up until he is laying on her, her mouth greedy on his, tasting herself on his mouth.

FROM THE NOVEL "THE NOSTALGIA FOR DESIRE"

He touches her face, gently, like a lover.

She holds him there, against the heat of her skin, her hands moving up and down his back, moulding him to all the places she has felt vacant for so long. Light fades out of the small round window above their heads.

When he enters her he tries to remember if it has happened before, but he remembers nothing.

Now we are strangers, she says. What we thought we knew about each other – you me and me you – all that has changed. What was at the centre of us, what was familiar is empty. I don't know you anymore. If you asked me what you are thinking right now I couldn't tell you. Half an hour ago, before this change, I would have said you are watching how in the lantern light the tablecloth is like a field, corrugated with tiny furrows that cup small shadows, thinking about your fingers half-curled on the top of the table, the skin hatched and coarse from exposure to gasoline and wind. Like leather. Now, where are we? It seems almost impossible for this to have happened, and yet there is also a feeling of inevitability to it. We have arrived here, at this table, like strangers. You hold the coffee mug differently. The mug is backward, cradled against your palm, two fingers slid through the handle and around the side. Also you never slump with your forehead on the butt of your hand, with your hair all twisted around in your fingers. Now I am also different. Now stories are arriving in my head. I feel dizzy. I need to tell someone how it could have happened. Maybe I have been waiting for years, for just this time. Everything swings inside me. It's going to come out. Stories come out when they are ready. My arms are like yellow sticks. All the air in the room packs into my lungs like damp cloth. So much air I can hardly breathe. The bigger my lungs get, holding all that air inside, the smaller yours get. You breathe so shallow I can't even see your chest move. Now you're not breathing at all. But your hands still move. Flexing.

The deeper you go, the less you know. Inside I'm all quicksand. We stay on the edges of each other, where it's safe. I know you, you say. I've been inside you, as deep as I could, you say, and that's still just the edge. We concentrate on a few surface details; the shape of a lip, the curve of a breast, an arm, scars we or someone else put there, the soft scruff at the back of a neck, incoherent memories of a time spent at some campground, fucking against the side of a car in a mountain parking lot, with warm breath at the corner of your eye – that is what and how we know. Your hands flex and some electrical current is driving those muscles and it has nothing to do with me. No memories, no history, nothing that I know. So we are strangers.

FROM THE NOVEL "THE NOSTALGIA FOR DESIRE"

He looks at the woman, her face given over to sleep, silent, asleep, like her hands. But all the time the spirit shows through the surface of the body, all over, so that each part bears witness in itself to the whole – the hands and the eyes, the curve of the belly and the face, the breasts and the sex, the legs and the arms, the breath, the heart, the temples, the temples and time.

There is the body of desire, and there is the body of the familiar. These two bodies are sometimes one flesh, but are never self-identical. Make no mistakes. No matter how often visited the body of desire resists your touch. A dark hand flexing inside your head. Desire shadowing the flesh. This is what you cannot finally hold. Memory is not desire. You cannot recognize the body of desire. It is forever third person, at a distance, unmarked and unmarkable, cloaked perhaps in a figurative if not literal darkness, clothed, or at a distance, so that knowing is impossible, and all is the pleasure of the mind. The mind moves over the body of desire, searching for a way inside, into, the impenetrable barrier of skin, but is unable to find entry. Your hands move desperately up and down, or they move casually up and down, like lovers' hands would.

The body of the familiar is open to you. Perhaps the body of desire sometimes flashes through, perhaps never, but the body of the familiar is what your hands know without excitement, without joy, and yet with a pleasing sense of content. It is a map you trace and retrace with five or six always repeated routes.

There is a quiet knocking above his head, and when he looks up the man's face is pressed against the smeared window, looking in at them on the damp bunk.

FROM THE NOVEL "THE NOSTALGIA FOR DESIRE"

GERALDINE MONK

OUTTHOUGHTS OF CHATTOX

As the hill imperceptibly steepened

and dimmed

the invisible squadrons

multiplied to

fever

pitch beating

deep and

crammed

against themselves and each

pitched

at the plagued

inner roof of my skull

browning

bruised with the spray

of ceaseless distress

trying to

out

to be aired and wing-ing

(it is the way of words –

to leave yet

to remain:

to breed in

absence:

in the immaculate

space of decay.

FROM "INTERREGNUM"

So my name
became
my curse (or vice versa
it doesn't really matter:
egg-chicken-chicken-egg-chickadee-
chickabiddy-biddychatter-chatterbox-
Chattox-

Chatter shivered
from my toothless mouth
and thin
senior citizen lips –
each word
(as is their way –
elbowing its turn
to shine and
astonish.

But only I was amazed
by my outbreaks of
quirky
metaphors and
unchallengeable leaps to
lucidity
at invention that beggared
hypocrisy
and most of all
at how my mind
could fold in on a

pure

unstressed monotone of

silence

when all around me

raged.

OUTTHOUGHTS OF MOULDHEELS

I swear

folk dropped dead either side

of curse – they had a tendency to –

we didn't invent mortality

death came regardless

but the mind slavers – turns cannibal –

chance is connected – devoured

throats hurt – constrict

the inflamed lump of raw foresight –

swallow and keck

swallow and keck

keck.

Unfussed as always the

dead bled fresh blood –

I swear

they needed no encouragement from us –

willingly – with gasp

the shrieking and the

foul yelling

sucked out

long

at last

ANNE WHITTLE REPLIES

a deal more

crafty than

uz

they knew

things never

uttered

in words

arms length and

longer than a

think

thi med id up·

and coming out

with things never

born

till pushed and named

from their gobs

lying

withershins

they knotted uz proper

in tittle-tattle

&

chains

*

straight up they

crawled

between our brain-curls and

FROM "INTERREGNUM"

        pin-winkled out
              ower
        tight black slugs of
        monosyllables

KATHERINE HEWIT REPLIES

It hurt.   Being
felled by a blunt brain.
A nincompoop
pokin iz nosey
wi manicured nails
tapered to cynical infinity;
Pin pointy dead onz.
Ten witherin sticks to taunt.

E was nowt budda Jimmy-bum-licker.
E lived down't lane in a big owse
wi iz porky fatted fingers drippin
rings and blottin copy
after nervous copy – and for what?
A right royal smile?
The patronising smirk of
ultimate noble birth to charm iz drab
and impotent circle.

A could ave pushed iz supper up
for't grief and sufferin e set in motion
and time trapped eternity.
A could ave done a lot o things – hypothetically –
with water mirrors and half moons A could ave
gagged the snotty little bugger
talkin down iz nose

FROM "INTERREGNUM"

talkin do-dah-lah-di like
talkin do-dah-lah-di.

ELIZABETH DEVIZE REPLIES

Your nightmares spilled over
and sucked me in.
Couldn't wake you.
No, couldn't wake myself but
the dead stirred slightly
on the third scream
and the days became dark
without centre
or sense.

One visit
to this reality
has been enough for me
with its ways and means
of making us
chalk words of desperation before
smashing the slate
clean
into the face of
oncoming
dawns
and all my born dreary days to this
ever nearing death of
laughable proportions
this trumped up charge of nothing
to nowhere

FROM "INTERREGNUM"

but your fantasies of flight
and ugly imaginings.

THE BULCOCKS REPLY

Between the sigh and the relief
the floor caved
and we danced on air
prematurely
the river was not human,
northern clouds were stuffed
with hills and mountains,
the mother's son
the son's mother still.

Between the Not and the Guilty
they switched the rules
so anyone
could swing along to
non sense
and separated the same
the related
at will
– a giftie bunch –
we handed em that
– a bunch o' bastards –
we handed em that an
all
the fat earth wobbled
on its imaginary
axis.

FROM "INTERREGNUM"

OUTTHOUGHTS OF DEMDIKE

My pictures of clay:
They were my art.
Not the pitch and toss of play or-
Sunday pleasure painting
but the teasing of spirit into the
dumb foxed earth.

It was the best and finest art
(a speedy way to make or take a life)
I spiked it with droplets of wonder
to be drunk unwittingly by children
and bring small animals to rest...

...the crest of my days...my life...
solitary moments...by the banks of the
Ribble and Calder I sat me down and chuckled
and sometimes wept...but mostly screwed up
my face into balls of exquisite contentment.

Oh certainly the images cried.
It is the way of clay.
Wetness...oozing through fingers...
make-believe eyes running...
to the far-off alarm call of birds.

I dried them. Fixed them. Thornpricked them.

FROM "INTERREGNUM"

Then sat well back and waited for the
diabolical climate to heighten.
Obliterate.

ALL REPLY

What was that jingle?
'Now the book is open spread
 Now the writing must be read
 Which condems'
What did it mean?

The impenetrable is impenetrable
until penetrated:
the mind could not grasp this
but
the gentle downrush of a sigh
the (transfixing) power of pain
the absolute (   ) ness of pain
this
it could grasp:
as memory became moment became memory
and the mouth opened wide with a shuddering
with a split / dawn / realisation
     – daming the vastness –
          utterness
        out and outness
          speechutter
          word chains
the mind could not
          can not bear
it slidslides back into trivia;

imbecilic elation.

Just ad(d) jingle.

ALAN MOORE

RECOGNITION

Heat, fierce and lurid, cooks the hunched hotel-room shadows into boiling ink. Old water spits and sizzles from the radiator joints, their copper fittings thick as vertebrae and leaking dirty steam. A blind is drawn across the room's one window closing out the Boston night, adorned with faded robins, bleached vines and the memory of flowers. Here is the ragged wheeze of sulphur-bitten lungs. Here are the woman's muffled squeals, made down her nose.

The sallow, vaguely foreign-looking manager is standing by the wardrobe, queerly still, gas-mantle stuttering on the wall behind him splashing careless light upon his back, a yellow urinary glaze upon his oiled black hair, its slick topography. His Easter Island face is lost in shadow, save there, where the gaslight catches on his glistening cheek and errant muscle twitches. By the door, the Cuban maid turns off her hearing aid and swallows hard against the parching heat. She grips the tunic of the bell-boy beside her, digging four grey nails into his sleeve while he sips hesitantly from a pale blue cocktail cigarette that's balanced in the other hand. His uniform, a threadbare Burgundy, is tainted with a sickly orange by this wan, uneven light and half unbuttoned down the front, blotched dark with gin. Stood in the juddering mantle-glow, their shadows cringe amongst the huge primeval flowers disfiguring the sweltered wallpaper. They stare towards the bed.

The Devil, red as tamarind, kneels in a rose of sweat-fogged sheets between the woman's arsenic-whitened thighs. His hairless body glistening as though freshly painted, one raw hand about each of her ankles where damp mocha hose is bunched. Her hands are bound with salmon shreds of nightgown to the condensation-beaded metal of the bed-head, fingers opening and closing like the thin limbs of albino crabs kept too long from the light. Balled up into a fist of silk her underwear is crammed into her mouth so that her cheeks bulge like an infant's. One suspender, spittle-silvered, has escaped the parted lips to trail across her chin.

He pulls her onto Him, onto His frilled crustacean shaft and her vagina steams. Convulsed by great magnetic shudders He is roaring, snorting like a murdered horse as He ejaculates, an orgasm of jewels

FROM THE COLLECTION "YUGGOTH CULTURES"

that floods her womb with Turquoise, Jade and Chrysolite. Salt streams of Beryl and Jacinth run down between her legs, the blue-ticked mattress turned to a cathedral-glass of brilliant stains. The bell-boy clears his throat.

Up in the hotel room above, the travelling salesman, Winfield Lovecraft, kneels there with his ear pressed to the radiator pipe and hears it all. Behind clenched eyelids, luminous paretic visions swarm; provide the feverish tableaus that he cannot see. He listens while the devil and the hotel staff take turns to fuck his wife. Tears big as thunder-spots fall from his burning cheeks to splash against the flecked linoleum. This is his punishment: he'd never dreamed that Susan might be hurt.

Those long and cock-sore weeks, what was a man to do? A wife who sat there at her bedroom mirror working creams into the skin beneath her cheek-blades, face already pallid, clay-like. She refused to touch him. On the road, the women hoboes sat astride his lap for cigarettes, and farmer's daughters, just like in the jokes. One night in Marblehead that waitress with the bruised and skinny legs, not quite fifteen, had let him take her face down on a sprawling, dog-eared tumble of *Judge* magazines stacked underneath the stairs, exquisitely cross-hatched caricatures imprinted faintly in reverse upon her sweat-glazed belly, on her breasts.

Downstairs the chanted protest of the bedsprings is commenced once more and viral imagery is seething in the dark behind the salesman's eyelids, overlays of spirochetal consciousness; alien signals flickering along the raddled spine. He rises, stumbles to the window in his shirt-sleeves, pant suspenders trailing in loose intestinal loops to either side. Hooking his nicotined fingers underneath the jamb he wrenches up the heavy glass, dust-frosted on the one side, rain-smeared on the other; bows a slurred screech from the sash, its single vocal cord.

The third-floor prospect overlooks the rear of the hotel, dog-trodden yards where toppled refuse bins lay beached in typhous dunes, the tidal debris lapping all about them: bottle glass that glints up from drenched cinder like a constellation fallen on hard times; suggestive knots of rag; the emptyings of chamber-pots. The window yawns, inhales, draws sweet and septic breath into the room. Planting his hands upon the blistered, sarcomatous paintwork of the sill he leans into the rotten night, a weather-eaten figurehead, lips barnacled with sores.

The words spill fierce and brilliant, a fan of white sparks shearing from a lathe, malarial poetry, hoarse canticles of ruin, abject glossolalia. They fucked his wife, the Devil and the bell-boy; came in spurts of coloured smoke across her poison-livid belly. It was all his fault, his punishment spelled in abandoned dresses strung along the roadside, rented cunts in rented rooms. Shaking and retching now he voids their names into the black, a gingham litany of women named for flowers, and saints, and executed queens.

Below, a window opens. Grey perfumes of broiling offal ribbon out through febrile mists above the garbage; tangle in blowfly trajectories. The pushy little wop downstairs is yelling for him to shut up, just shut the fuck up but he can't, he can't, there's so much more to tell, about his wife, her distant monologues upon their little girl until he'd had to slap her, *Susan, he's a boy! A little boy!* Her father, old man Whipple Phillips with his headaches, forehead purple, raging at his son-in-law when first he learned of Winfield's indiscretions. All of this the salesman bellows, out across the silent roofscape, scraps of echo snagging in the eaves.

Someone is hammering on the door, but nothing stems his pentecostal stream, chin wet from slobbered consonants. He is the monstrous father and his cheeks bulge with new syllables; a dreadful tertiary language that his son will one day echo in the loathsome coinages he picks to name his pantheon, his only children. From the open window of his hotel room, Yog Sothoth howls into the world's stink; roars and roars into the human dark.

In 1933, some thirty-five years later, Howard Lovecraft, in a letter to his friend James Morton, claims light-heartedly to be descended from his Elder deities: from Azathoth, Cthulhu and Yog Sothoth. There, four years before his end, he almost managed to decrypt the bas-reliefs raised in the R'lyeh of his sunken mind; almost exposed the Lurker at the Threshold as a travelling salesman, nothing more. Would he have screamed his father's name, like Wilbur Whately's brother, from a hilltop: College Hill, or Sentinel? Would he have recognized himself, his nature and his mannerisms captured in the frail, fore-doomed procession of his fictive victims; his narrators, driven mad or torn apart by Old Ones, things that suppurate and bellow in the sloughs of night?

"The body shrieked at me with a dead cry,
And all too late I knew that it was I!"

FROM THE COLLECTION "YUGGOTH CULTURES"

ZAMAN'S HILL

Moonfire, decanted by huge, prehistoric machinery into the die of the hills, quenched to lead and by day the far slopes lost in steam. Birdless dark in the pine-deeps. Toboggan scars drop from the path into haunted, perpetual twilight and down to the lake; the drowned hamlets beneath a vast acid lagoon, void of fish. Shreds of wallpaper drift in the submarine kitchens, a memory of waterweed.

Mineral energies sucked up like snot through the bronchial roots taint the sap with old grudge, coded Thatcher-year sunlight deciphered in camp-fire to ash and to spark. Soon we all reek of flame with its taste in our water, an Inferno cordial.

We stare at the bright fissured hide of the firelogs, red-hot alligators crawled from a burned Nile, breathing smoke, we inhale the wood's madness, the contour-mapped rings of its DNA memory encrypted the length of each bark-armoured spine, so that some of us know a compulsion to sleep in the gut of the blaze, or to give it our blood, and the twelve-year-olds skirmish with bottles and toasting forks.

Somehow the crotch of a woman is sculpted, a split stump with knickers pulled up the fork, a crude amputee idol that calls to the ghost-dogs who scrawl canine histories, written in piss in her flank.

These are Machen-hills, skull-hollow, echoing reverie of skeleton, arrow-head; fossil imperatives; grey-lobed with slate; webbed by ganglion worms. The intent of this landscape is buried: immense geological crania, stratified sentience under the scalp-grass, military crew-cut of Forestry trees.

In pursuit of the cortex, the bedrock of purpose and memory we must go deeper, explore the decalcified brain's subterranea, down through the nightmaring stone to a secret Pre-Cambrian core: Dan Yr Ogof, a limestone delirium three hundred million years old, its grey matter shot through by the tetanus vein of the Llynfell, whose calcinous rivulets spread like a tectonic syphilis birthing slow, massive hallucinations that accrue, centimetres to measure the centuries, limaform visions of Moonmilk and Helectite, strange half-complete hypnagogic impressions of possible life-forms chewed into the calcite, stained bloody or yellow as tallow by iron, dyed pale statue-grey by the manganese.

FROM THE COLLECTION "YUGGOTH CULTURES"

Here is an underland coral remembering long-vanished tropical ocean, the reefs of Primordia. Here are the mudflowers grown into a hideous Michelin man, a toad-figurine, white and obese, head half melted with rain-eaten eyes.

Knots of tentacle coil from the underlit scarp where the flowstones and curtains form jellyfish rills and a gigantic femur, two-thousand-year-old alabaster stood knee-socket deep in a rockpool. The stone threatens terrible life, dreams of meat, draped like fat in streaked translucent veils from the underhang; fashions a geo-organic menagerie, every conceivable quirk of biology prefigured here in these waxed carboniferous ruptures, this hog-bristle stubble of stalactite, fat roe of cave pearls. In shower-spattered streets below ground, dim, pellucid, our fingers trace wet shapes: the cold, pregnant message of R'lyeh.

JEREMY REED

ZAMORA INSTITUTE

He inserts a mauve contact lens and checks
his reconstructed features; collagen
implants, liposuction; he's angular
and out-profiles Michael Jackson.
Outside, a metal tree shaped like a star

scintillates in the dangerous UV light.
A child sits in a sculpted conifer
and walkie-talkies his robotic toy.
The real park lions are lobotomized.
The big one sleeps curled up on a parked car.

And daily, new arrivals come to stay
and attend lectures. They will recreate
themselves; dismantle knowledge of their past,
adopt names given by their instructors
and stand outside a compression-sealed gate

awaiting admission into a cult
for the re-formed. No-one may ever speak
of the initiation. Some remain
inside for years and return as children
who walk off fearless across a dust plain

towards the lost cities; the fabled worlds
where earlier ancestors lived and died.
He checks his memory loss on a screen,
the red digits read cancelled and the green matter
to be revised. The optimum

is 0.5 green. And still the children play
their adult games before lectures, and ten
analysands strike out beneath the trees,
headed for pre-initiation jabs
they walk clean through the sleeping lion's den.

FROM "KICKS"

TAXI TO THE END OF THE WORLD

And it was nothing, so the driver said,
digesting elephant steaks or zebra,
his stomach open like a corolla
discussing protein, toxins, Manhattan,
extreme eating because the planet's dead,

and he'd be going back after this ride
to the old cities, his box apartment.
"Someone's got to stay": my presentiment
was of looting, fisting out diamonds
from display cards. Our wheels skirted the tide

and there were cattle and a family
knee-deep in water looking for a place
to cross; a bridge sunk beneath the surface
of rising waters. We went into hills,
making a detour to meet with the sea

on the last coast. The man spoke of nomads,
straggling tribes who had marched on the desert
listening for instructions, ways to alert
themselves to power, and of politicians
making suicide-pacts on pyramids.

We passed the first shacks put up on this coast.
Numeral calculations done in blood
were wildly calligraphized on white wood.
A lion-tamer instructed his child,
a group of long-haired men sat around lost;

and here the taxi stopped, he wouldn't go
right to the end, and he was obstinate.
He spoke of dangers and he had a date
that evening; love and barbecued camel,
one of the last from a blackmarket zoo.

HART CRANE

The big push, manic overdrive, Hart Crane
in South Street, Sand Street, cruising for sailors,
his pocketbook blotched by whiskey, night rain
to inky thumbprints, doodled stars and stripes
and love-hearts. A gangster suit, orange tie,
he feeds off his reckless dichotomy –
the tempestuous visionary who hypes

his disordered senses until they push
language to the ruthless frontiers of sex,
and then by day at Sweets, slowing the rush,
the advertising copy clerk still hung over,
a cheroot snaking smoke into his eye,
and Grace and Grandma demanding letters
in his lunchbreaks. He is a cooked lobster,

hard-shelled already, a grey brush of hair
outgrown the black; rashed vesicles, a wild
impulsive maudit swinging on the air
of New York jazz, imploding poetry
to Ravel's Bolero, played sixty times
to heighten mania; and how the power was there
in the compressed, metaphoric vitality

to stand out as distinctly new, a way
of having the poem hold up and keep
a skyscraper view of the century.
Pugnacious, dangerous as a Russian bear
when overlit, thrown in a Paris jail,
dusted by New York cops, Hart's mad rampage
burnt out his gift. We feel his late despair,

poetic impotence, his poverty
unrelieved by his father's candy Life Saver,
his volcanic storms shaking white-hot ash
over his friends. His style was to sever
with every obstruction, give up the page
for self-debasement, kneeling down to blow

some anonymous, car-parking stranger,

and violently shipping out from the States
for a tequila-fired nerve-jab at Mexico,
it seemed the inevitable exit,
a last desiccated fish-gasp to write
the vision down; and reversed, coming back
he tilted overboard at noon, his white
shirt puffed before the water smacked it slack.

MAP MAKING

It's about reinvention, star clusters
expanding into redshift, light signals
travelling away from the universe,
and how the ordinary is transformed,
the street corner curves suddenly into
a town called Hexagram, an eight-sided,
forested place there for discovery,
its people listening to an eighth sense
with the immediacy of radio,
and on the outskirts there's a crystal sea
through which one views proliferating ferns,
riotous fauna, exploding seed pods
turning that instant into flowers. And words
convey the transformation. I can see
three separate skies, a white, a green, a red,
form a triptych, three windows into space,
an expansive cosmogony.
Nothing's fixed, or identifiable
except by how it changes, the wonder
of making maps for alternative worlds,
the real ones in which imagery
stands out like markings on the ocelot,
and the way forward leads out of a line
into a spiral, takes me where snowflakes
are shaped like strawberries and fall red-hot.

FROM "KICKS"

STAR-MAP

A purple curtain's drawn in the white house
opposite. An invading clump of trees
is often the dark blue-green that Magritte
uses to lodge a crescent moon
in foreshortened perspective.
                    "We're like that,"
you say, "we blank out visuals for the surety
of space we turn to secrecy;
and what will happen if we go too far
inside the private fantasies
with which we instruct each other?" A star
is visible above their house,
a mineral starfish twinkling glacially.
It's the coming of a compact blue night.

They've left a red chair on the balcony
where she suns in the afternoon, dress off,
dark glasses, a minimal bikini.
Beyond that house the air is wider still
for no obstruction – it is grass country,
a wind that smells of horses. We let in the dark

and watch their screened off privacy.
Later, we'll revert to parameters
which are our own confinement, and pretend
we can still see their house and beyond that
a star-map open to a conjectural end.

STRETCH

The spider's highwire elasticity,
tuning resonant strings, tightening a chord
strung up from its umbilical and pitched,
is one way of expansion, turning out
the inner, so it's recognizable –

the pattern's articulated that way.
Count to a thousand from the toe to knee,
my pointed tongue picks out the lozenges
in each fishnet stocking you wear,
black mesh demanding I go higher and explore
the insides of your thighs,
the soft flesh there. We used to drive across
a curved suspension bridge, one bank of town
to the other, a green river
making fast tracks beneath. We love like that,
our nerve-endings feeling for subtle links,
a way from inside to be each other
at the interior. And when you come,

this means stretching to reach the highest note,
the one that has you bunch and ripple free
in scales so individual
they need notation as a score.
I know you then as vocable, your toes
sensitised, struggling in black net,
the spider on the window tugging hard
to fix a line, leaving the tie point float.

FROM "KICKS"

BURROUGHS

Bullet holes pepper the shotgun painting –
a yellow shrine with a black continent
patched up on wood.
The suit's impeccable, no lazy tie,
the knot perfect between blue collar points,
a grey felt hat tilted back off the head,
the face vulturine, eyes which have stepped in
to live with mental space and monitor

all drifting fractal implosions;
the man is easy in his Kansas yard,
his GHQ since 1982,
the New York bunker left behind, and cats
flopping around his feet, finding the sun,
picking up on psi energies.

He's waiting for extraterrestrials,
psychic invasion; we can bypass death
by shooting interplanetary serum.
Some of us are the deathless ones. He pours
a crippling slug of Jack Daniels.
The body can't function without toxins
of weird metabolic fluctuations.
He's waiting for the big event.

And has become a legend, now a myth,
a cellular mythologem.
His double's pressure-locked in the psyche,
for fear he blows a fuse, goes out on leave
and kills. He is invaded by Genet,
his presence asks for love, for completion.
The man wanders to his tomato patch;
his amanuensis snatches a break.
The light is hazy gold. He'll outlive death,
be here when there's no longer a planet.

MAN CONDEMNED TO DEATH
A translation of
***Le Condamné A Mort** by Jean Genet*

The wind rolling a heart over concrete,
a sobbing angel hooked inside a tree,
the azure column breaking marble down
open emergency exits in my night.

A poor bird dying and the taste of ash,
an eye remembered sleeping on the wall,
and this aching fist menacing the sky
have your face crumple in my hollow hand.

This face that's hard yet lighter than a mask
weighs more in my palm than the flashing jewel
pocketed by loose fingers. Smudged with tears,
it's dull and fierce. A bouquet covers it.

Your face is stern, with a Greek shepherd's tan,
its impulses quiver in my locked grip.
Your eyes are roses above a dead woman's mouth,
and your archangel's nose is like a beak.

If your voice sings, then was it real evil
glittered like frost, inciting you to crime,
your hair scintillating with steel-blue stars,
your forehead crowned with thorns from a rosebush?

Tell me what mad distress shatters your sight
with such despair that the ferocious pain
gone crazy, personified, rings your mouth
despite frozen tears, with a twisted smile?

Don't sing "Bullies Of The Moon" tonight.
Blond-haired kid, be a princess in a tower
dreaming introspectively of our love
or a tight-jeaned cabin-boy up on deck.

PREVIOUSLY UNPUBLISHED

He comes down to the bridge towards evening
and sings "Ave Maria stella" to those
clone-headed sailors kneeling on the job,
each holds a throbbing cock in a tight fist.

They're waiting to fuck you outrageous blond kid
these muscled sailors straining in their pants.
My love, *mon amour*, will you steal the keys
which open up the sky where the mast rocks

and where you sow white blessings royally
as snow on my page in this dormant cell.
Terror's the dead choked over by violets,
death with black roosters and bloodless lovers.

A prowling guard pads by on velvet feet.
Your memory floods like colour to my eyes.
We can make an exit over the roof.
They say that Guiana sizzles in the heat.

O the sweetness of impossible islands,
delusional skies, the sea and the palms,
transparent mornings, mad evenings, calm nights,
heads that are shaved, and satin skins.

Let's dream together, love, of a hoodlum,
big as the universe, body splashed with tattoos.
He'll strip us, lock us into bondage cells,
and show us how between his golden thighs

and on his smoking stomach, a hot pimp
works it up on carnations and jasmine,
petals that tremble when his glowing hands
and kisses hurry along a prized thigh.

Such sadness in my mouth. A bitter pain
bursting the waters in my heart. I see
my perfumed loves are leaving, they have heavy balls.
My strangled voice cries after every prick.

PREVIOUSLY UNPUBLISHED

Stop singing, kid, your streetwise manners jar,
be a young girl with a pure radiant throat,
or if you dare, a child singing lyrics
dead in me till the blade cuts off my head.

Beautiful youth crowned with lilacs,
lean over me, and let my rising cock
smack the foundation on your cheek. Your killer boy
will tell you his story as he explodes.

He sings he had your body and your face
and your heart no eagle's claws will tear open.
What I would do to adopt your round knees,
your cool neck, your soft hand. To be your age.

To fly, to fly to your blood-spattered sky
and to make a single masterpiece of the dead
gathered here and there in meadows, the dead
dazzling to prepare his teenage heaven...

Oppressive mornings, rum, and cigarettes,
tobacco shadows, jail, lonely sailors
visit my cell where a psychopath's ghost
presses me hard against his bulging fly.

The song travelling through the underworld
is a pimp's cry carried away by your voice,
the song of a hanged man gone marble-stiff,
the enchanted call of a thief in love.

The teenager asleep calls for life-buoys
no sailor throws to the panicked sleeper.
A child rests upright, glued against the wall,
another sleeps in convoluted knots.

I've killed for blue eyes and indifferent looks
which never understood my restrained love.
In a black gondola an unknown lover
died adoring me in the autumn rain.

PREVIOUSLY UNPUBLISHED

And when you're hyped up, ready for the kill,
features gone cold, head tousled with blond hair,
then to a wild cadence of violins
you'll slit the throat of a rich debutante.

An iron knight will appear on the earth,
impassive and cruel and visible to all
in the imprecise gesture of a sad old woman.
Don't flick an eyelash when he glares at you.

This apparition drops from a redoubtable sky
of love's crimes. Child of the depths
astonishing beauty will come from your body,
and perfumed shooting-stars burn from your cock.

That's a black granite rock on the carpet,
one hand on the hip. Just hear him walk.
Go for the sun of his free-sex body
and stretch out quietly at his fountain's rim.

Each bloodfeast assigns a beautiful boy
to serve as back-up in the child's first try.
Appease your anguish, totally let go,
suck my hard cock as you would an ice lolly.

Gently nibble the cock shaving your cheek,
kiss the swollen head, cram the whole thing down,
work it into deep throat, and swallow it.
Strangle yourself with love, spit out hot pearls.

Adore my tattooed body on your knees,
lean and aspiring as a totem pole.
My cock will break you like a weapon primed
for worship, pushing for the tightest fit.

It springs right to your eyes, and rips your soul.
Lower your lips and watch it telescope,
and seeing it so eruptively taut,
you pout a kiss at it, and say "Madame."

PREVIOUSLY UNPUBLISHED

Madame, listen to me. Madame we're dying here.
The manor is haunted, and the prison rocks.
We're moving into space, take us away
to your room in the sky, Lady of mercy.

Call the sun out to come and comfort me,
strangle the roosters, dope the executioner.
The sun's anaemic outside my window,
prison's a school in which we learn to die.

Let your teeth slide their wolfish grin
into my unprotected neck. Your heart's
unmoved, by the light touch with which my hand
travels to complement that spot.

Come to me beautiful sun, and come my Spanish night,
burn in my eyes which will be dead tomorrow,
arrive, open my door, give me your hand,
lead me right out across the countrys.de.

Let the sky redden, and the stars break through,
all flowers open and bells reverberate,
and the black grass kneel to the morning dew
in meadows. As for me I'm bound to die.

Visit me rosy sky, my blond basket,
favour the man who is condemned to die.
The lacerating light will kill, climb, bite,
but softly place its cheek to my round head.

We hadn't finished speaking of love
or even finished smoking our Gitanes,
the court verdict seemed inconceivable,
the blond kid sentenced, blonder than the sun.

Love, come to my mouth. Love open your doors.
Flit through the halls, and lightly fly down stairs,
with the agility of a farmhand
riding the air like a flight of dead leaves.

PREVIOUSLY UNPUBLISHED

Walk through the walls, or if need be balance
on roof edges, the wild rim of the sea,
use any threat that works, or prayer,
be intermediary an hour before my death.

Murderers wrap themselves in the sunrise
inside my cell, the fir trees frisk like surf
engaged in a fine songline to sailors
taking a polish in the early light.

Who carved a windrose in the plaster?
Who in the depths of Hungary dreams of his home?
What child rolled over in my rotted straw
recalling friends, his split-second awake.

I'll let my madness free on a long lead
to build a consoling hell of soldiers,
stripped to the waist, and under green skivvies
pulling out heavy flowers with their thunderish smell.

Scare out from the back of the head insane
gestures, kidnap children, invent tortures,
mutilate beauty, grind her lost ideals,
transform Guiana to a gay rendezvous.

My old Maroni, and sweet Cayenne,
I see twenty faggots propped by the wall
next to the blond cutie extracting butts
the guards spit out into the flowers and moss,

a wet butt depresses us for the day.
Alone, erect above the rigid ferns,
the youngest faggot leans with a girl's hips,
passive, waiting for sex-rites to begin.

The old murderers rush to see this sight
and squatting down they draw from a dry stick
a little fire stolen by the blond kid
its movements purer than a stiffening prick.

PREVIOUSLY UNPUBLISHED

The toughest bandit with stacked up muscles
bows with respect before this fragile boy.
The moon climbs in the sky. A quarrel's set.
The black flag shivers in mysterious folds.

Your lace-fine gestures are like gossamer,
you lean, one shoulder up against a palm
and smoke. The inhalation spirals down
while all the convicts in a solemn dance,

silent and serious and each in turn
retrieve a fragrant wisp out of your mouth
one drop, not two, of the smoke on your tongue
rolling away. My triumphant brother,

evil, invisible divinity,
you sit there impassive, metallic, cold,
withdrawn into yourself and self-obsessed
raised on the edge of a hammock which sings.

Your delicate soul is spellbound in the hills
still following the crazy zigzag flight
of an escaped convict who ended up
shot through the lungs, crashing the valley floor.

Blond kid of mine, you fly right to the moon.
Decant into my mouth your heavy sperm,
roll it from your mouth through my teeth, my love,
finally fertilizing our wedding.

Fasten your ravished body to my own
that's worn out from excessive sex with youth.
Captivated, my hand fits your blond balls,
my black marble prick fills you to the heart.

Take aim at him standing in a burning sunset
that's going to scorch my heart. It won't take long,
come to me, if you dare, climb out of ponds
and swamps from which you blow bubbles.

PREVIOUSLY UNPUBLISHED

The souls of my dead. Burn me. Kill me.
Like Michelangelo I've carved a life
out of beauty, I've always served that cause,
my belly, my knees, my hands. And roses on my mind.

The roosters in the chicken coop, the Gallic lark,
the dairyman's milkcans, a bell in the air,
a step on the gravel, a window lit up white,
I nurture how the slate-grey prison shines.

I'm really not afraid. If my head rolls
like an apple smashed against your blond head,
I hope mine ends up resting on your hip
or for closer impact, chicken, on your neck.

Watch out, tragic king with your parted lips,
I've access to your arid sand gardens,
where you're jerking off with two fingers raised,
your head got under a blue linen veil.

Delirious, strung out, I see your double.
Love. Song. My queen. Is it a spooky man
I thought I saw in your playful white eyes
stares at me now out of the plaster wall?

Don't be too hard, let morning praise be sung
to your vagrant's heart. Give me a last kiss.
My God, I'll die without having once held
your body closely to my cock and heart.

Forgive me Lord, for I have sinned,
my tear-stained voice, my fever and my grief
this pain of exile from my lovely France,
won't it do Lord to have me lie at last
    a hobo collapsed

in your fragrant arms inside your ice palaces.
Lord of the dark I still know how to pray.
It's really me, father, who cried one day,
Glory to heaven and the god of thieves
    Hermes winging his way.

I ask of death the longest rest
the song of seraphim, perfumes, coiffed hair,
and cherubs wrapped up in blue woollen cloaks
and nights without a moon or sun
 black above immobile moors.

It's not today I'll die beneath the blade,
my respite's temporary. A floor above
my lazy pet, my pearl, my stomping kid
awakes. And with his army boots he'll stamp
 right across my grizzled skull.

It seems an epileptic raves next door,
the prison percolates an elegy.
I think of sailors making a lost port,
and convicts dreaming of a new America.

PREVIOUSLY UNPUBLISHED

SIMON WHITECHAPEL

XERAMPELINAE

In due course the trial took place and in due course Philomel Thanatophore was convicted of the murder. She was sentenced to hang. No appeal was made. In the second week of her internment before serving of sentence she wrote an impassioned letter to the famous Colombian detective Bacco di Corona, enclosing a photograph of herself. Di Corona was entering on that stage of his career in which success and fame had begun to enervate, and the letter captured his attention from the first. The case seemed an entirely hopeless one, and Philomel Thanatophore was a very beautiful young woman, with the face – so he said to himself – of mingled nobility and depravity, like that of a sad fellatrix in a minor provincial court in the latter days of Rome. He was then occupied with several cases, some of the very highest importance. To discard them in favour of one of this nature would be an act almost as capricious as it was foolish. He would offend clients of long standing, and lose a great deal of money.

He began work on the case at once.

He obtained an interview with the convicted woman with some difficulty. She was pale, and seemed to have lost a good deal of weight. Di Corona wore a dove-grey suit, cut with exquisite taste, and showing to best advantage the slim, muscular lines of his forty-eight year frame. His shoes were highly polished and he wore a single pale rose in his button hole, which, with a smile and shallow, graceful bow, he plucked forth and offered to his prospective client as she entered the room in which he awaited her. She, a little bewildered, accepted the rose. He took her arm – she shuddered a little under the contact, as though his palm were hot or cold or electrically charged – and propelled her gently into a chair. He faced her, his eyes moving gently over her face for perhaps a minute. Then he bent over her, taking her shoulders in his hands so that she could not move away from him, and asked, staring deeply into her eyes: "Are you innocent?"

She did not reply. A single tear welled in her left eye and ran down her cheek. He smiled. He rode the possibilities of the moment, judging what best to do next, then, with perfect timing, loosened one hand and slapped her gently, once, twice, three times, then clutched her to himself, and whispered into her ear as delicately as though he tipped poison there, "Are you innocent?"

He felt her chin, smooth and round and cold as stone, slide slowly up and down and up on his own smooth and scented cheek. He released her, rose, bowed, and left. He was quite unaware what course he would pursue to establish the innocence of his client and trusted entirely to chance. That night he dined early and alone, smoked a single cigar in the garden, and then locked himself into the library. On the table he laid out a huge and complicated game of patience, which seemed to him, as he coaxed movement here and there in the bright patternings of cards, like a model of the circulatory system of a vast and decrepit demon, the ichor of whose veins has stilled mostly, and is stirred to life only in brief spasms and patches at the memory of the delight of ancient evils. At intervals he was prompted by the cards to remove volumes from the shelves, and to read pages of these. What he read seemed entirely fragmentary and unconnected, but he committed it carefully to memory, and resisted the urge to smoke a second cigar out of a vague notion that he was bound to abstinence in his performance of a semi-occult ritual.

At a quarter to midnight he closed the volume he was reading and bent with fierce concentration over the patience, promising himself that if he finished the game before midnight he would reward himself with the body of the new undermaid. At five minutes past the final card fell into place, but he was in no mood to deny himself. Even the fact, discovered later in his room when she was delivered to him, that the girl was menstruating, seemed of little importance, and he took her three times in the night, *per vas nefandum*, sleeping deeply and quietly after each act, which he prolonged with skill and gentleness, though more to his own satisfaction than to the girl's. In the morning she fellated him, with squeaks of commingled delight and disgust at the taste of her own dried shit upon the head of his member, and a sun seemed to burst inside his skull at the moment of orgasm, as though portending success for his newest case.

When he had dressed and breakfasted he took up a railway timetable and thrust a pin into it. He then called for a dice and rolled a five. He turned to page five and discovered the pin had decided that he would travel that day to the hamlet of Market Blandings. He made several telephone calls, arranged for the dismissal of the new undermaid, and left to catch his train at twelve o'clock, taking with him his gentleman's gentleman and sufficient luggage to supply his needs for an indefinite number of days. By four o'clock he was established in the guest room of the Bull and Partridge. After a small glass of absinthe in the bar he took a walk outside. Within fifteen minutes he found himself at the summit of a small hill, looking down onto fifty or so acres of well-tended parkland and an Elizabethan manor house.

He subsided onto the grass, which was damp, though not excessively so, and opened his cigarette case. But he had forgotten his matches. He closed the ease with a sigh of irritation and was about to return it to his pocket when a voice said, "Need a light?"

He looked around and saw a youth standing a few yards off, flushed, and holding onto the saddle and cross-bar of a bicycle, which he had apparently just pushed up the slope of the hill on the side opposite to the manor house.

"Well, as a matter of fact – I do," he replied. The youth let the bicycle fall and walked to where di Corona sat. He produced a matchbox and with a careless sequence of gestures conjured a flame. Di Corona re-opened his cigarette case and removed a cigarette.

"Care for one yourself?" he asked.

"No. I'm fine, thank you."

He lit the cigarette from the proffered flame and drew on it, looking up with a smile into the flushed face of the youth, who stood looking down at him, then said, "You're foreign, aren't you?"

"Yes. How can you tell?"

The youth sat down beside him, resting himself on one elbow, and spat towards the bicycle, one of the wheels of which was still revolving from the carelessness with which he had let it fall.

"Oh, not by your accent. By your hair, I think. It's so black."

Di Corona smiled. He drew again on the cigarette and turned his face away from the youth to release the smoke.

"Don't mind me," said the youth. "I used to smoke myself, a while ago. Gave up."

"Why?"

"I fell in love."

"Who with?"

"That's not grammatical English."

"No, but it's colloquial. With whom?"

"With her." The youth nodded towards the manor house.

"Who's she?"

"She's...she's nobody you could possibly know."

"Is she beautiful?"

"Yes, very. But cruel, very cruel. I want to have sex with her, you know. She's very clever, too, you know, but I'm not interested in her mind. Only in her body. She's so tall and slim and her hair is a sort of moony gold. God, how I hate and how I want her."

"Well, can't you have her?"

"No, she won't let me."

"Have you asked her?"

"Yes, lots of times. Lots of times."

The youth stood up suddenly. Di Corona noticed that there was a bulge in his trousers. He stood looking down towards the house, his hands flexing minutely. He walked towards the bike and picking it up swung his leg over the cross-bar to stand astride it. Di Corona threw his cigarette away.

"So, what are you going to do?" he asked.

"Do you see that wall down there?"

"Yes."

At the foot of the hill, running to left and right to encircle the parkland in which the house was set, was a tall wall of red brick topped with iron *fleur-de-lys*.

"I'm going to ride my bike down into it."

Di Corona got quickly to his feet.

"But you'll hurt yourself," he said.

"No, I won't," said the youth, pushing himself off down the hill. "I'll kill myself."

He leaned forward, lifting his feet to the pedals, concentrating on guiding the front wheel downhill through the thick grass. The bike began to pick up speed.

Di Corona stood watching. He cupped his hands around his mouth and shouted, "But who is she?"

The youth was half-way down the hill. He had lifted his feet wide and clear of the pedals, which whirred like wings. Hearing di Corona's voice he twisted to look back. He was smiling.

"My sister!" he shouted. He turned to guide the bike again. It was travelling very fast when it ran into the wall and he had leant forward well over the handlebars to receive the stern kiss of the brick on his face. Di Corona wanted to smoke another cigarette, but feeling disinclined to walk down the hill to find the matchbox in the pockets of the corpse he returned to his room and smoked there.

That evening he made several further phone-calls. He went to bed early but did not sleep until two or three in the morning. The following day he retraced his route to the summit of the hill. The bicycle and the youth's corpse were gone but it was still possible to trace the passage of the bicycle down the hill in an occasionally wavering line crushed out in the grass by the bicycle's wheels. There was also, he found when he had followed the line down the hill to the wall, a wide splash of blood on the brick, and a scrape of paint, vivid blue as a feather. He began to follow the wall to the left, and after a few minutes came across a pair of wide gates, half-opened, or half-closed. He paused, looking beyond them to the house, which lay two or three hundred yards away, then stepped between them.

He walked quickly, almost nervously, and found, as he rang the bell, that there was a knot of tension in his throat, that rode and hung on his efforts to swallow it away. For half-a-minute there was silence, then the sound of one, two, three footsteps on marble and the door swung open. Tall and slim and her hair was a sort of moony gold. Di Corona smiled, feeling, most uncharacteristically, a little bewildered, and presented his card.

"I am Bacco di Corona," he said. "Your brother and I met some time ago in London, and he invited me to call if I happened to be in the area. I am, and so, as you see, I have."

She did not look at the card, but held it firmly by one corner, as though with a flick she would lodge it in his heart or throat, and said, "Come in."

Di Corona followed her in the hall. She wore a dress twenty years out of fashion, its silk faded and streaked. Di Corona fancied that a face peeped at him from the flowers woven into her hair, goatishly puckered with malevolence. They drank tea in the parlour, and she said unsmiling, "My brother is dead. But of course, you know. And he has not been to London for seven or eight years."

"What is your name?" asked di Corona.

She shook her head.

"I am no-one you would know," she said.

"So, I ask. What is your name?"

"I cannot say. I think perhaps I have no name."

"Impossible."

She laughed, and asked, "But if I have no existence, then how can I have a name?"

"You doubt your own existence?"

"But of course. Do you not?"

"No."

"But you must. How can you be certain that you are not dreamed in the sleep of a god or demon?"

"I am certain that I am not. *Cogito, ergo sum.*"

"*Merde.* Your conviction has no basis. It is a bubble. Behold, I blow; and behold, it bursts."

Her lips pursed, and she blew, and di Corona found his existence without basis, and sensed beneath the melting foundations of his personality the stirring to wakefulness of a being vast and nebulous and wholly beyond his comprehension. She laughed, and stirred the smooth fleshy cylinders of her fingers. From the air, seeded and swelling from points of black, three lamiae grew, slim and tiny as children, with white, sweet faces, and pale thirsty tongues.

FROM THE UNPUBLISHED COLLECTION "DCLXVI"

"Ruth, Dorathée, Allath, drink, drink."

Wide gauzy wings flapped once, twice, and the three settled upon him, nuzzling his flesh with cold, prickling lips, and biting suddenly like frost. They gurgled and the girl laughed. She left the room and di Corona spoke, urgently, choosing the timbre and pitch of his voice with the greatest care.

"Allath."

The lamia drank on.

"Dorathée."

The lamia drank on.

"Ruth."

A stirring, then feline resumption of indifference.

"Ruth. Ruth. I love thee."

The face lifted, erubesced with his blood, and beyond the white crystal chips of teeth cold breath stirred.

"Lie."

"I love thee. Believe me, Ruth. Sweet Ruth."

From beyond, muffled a little by distance, a voice called.

"Drink, little sister, drink."

Sleepy with thirst, the head began to droop.

"Ruth. Ruth. I want to kiss thee, Ruth."

"Then kiss."

"How may I kiss when I am dead? Thy sisters drink my life away. Speak to them. They drink my love away. Speak."

The lamia clicked and hissed and her two sisters, slowly, their lips and chins threaded with blood, raised their heads.

"Kiss me, Ruth. I am weak. Kiss me."

She rose from her feeding place at his arm and flew to him. Her arms, skeletal and icy, encircled his neck and she dipped her face forward to his. He sealed his lips over hers and darted his tongue forward into her mouth, swiftly, tremblingly, as though he were a hummingbird at flower. She disgorged his blood and he drank, choking a little on its saltiness and chill. She withdrew her face and perched, watching him, on his chest.

"What is mine, thou hast returned. What is mine, I give to thee."

"Thy love?"

"Yes."

The lamia sighed.

"I have thy love? While the stars and moon may remain?"

"Yes."

She rose, singing, onto the air, and di Corona, a little weak still, stood and walked quickly from the room. He did not think the power of the girl extended beyond the house. At the door, he thought, *If it is locked*, but it opened easily and he stepped through, surprised to find that night had fallen and an owl, white and silent, drifted beneath the moon.

"Thou desertst me."

He turned, to see the lamia in the doorway, anguished, caught in insubstantial shadow. Her body ignited, burnt to ash, grew whole, ignited, burnt to ash, grew whole, and she screamed. On and on.

She said, "I can help thee."

"How?"

"Save me from my pain."

There were peppermints in his pocket. He said, "I suffer from neuralgia. I have a drug."

He tossed them to her and she snapped them from the air, one, two, three.

"How?"

"She has a key...."

"But the mechanism of her power?"

"I cannot tell thee. Quickly, for the pain returns, and I cannot endure it, though I must."

"Where is she?"

"She sleeps. Upstairs. Thou wilt know. Follow her scent."

He stepped back into the house, sweating with fear. The hall was dark, lit only by the flaring agony of the lamia. He found the stairs, and climbed them slowly, carefully, stopping at every seventh step to raise his head and draw air into his nostrils, slowly, carefully.

He could smell her, the salt, postdiluvian scent of arousal.

The door of her room was unlocked, a little open. and he could see, peering to catch a glimpse of her, the foot of her bed and a fold of grey silk, lit by a bar of moonlight from a single high window. He pushed the door open and entered. She lay fully clothed on the bed, arms crucified mockingly wide.

He asked, "Where is the key?"

"I have it," she said, opening her clenched hands. Half of a small rusted key lay like a nail-wound on each white palm.

"Give them to me."

"No," said she. "They are mine."

He jumped forward, too slow, and beneath the choking pressure of his hands he felt the final bobbing of her throat.

He throttled her unconscious, the faint smiling curve of her lips lost and regained as the colour of her face darkened to and beyond their redness, and released her to begin tearing strips of silk from her clothing.

Hands and feet he lashed her to the bed, and lifted back the scented tents of her skirts to expose the christ-memorial ΙΧΘΥΣ she wore between her thighs.

It awaited him, threaded with moisture, and its heat glowed upon his face as he leaned forward and pressed his lips to it. He breathed deeply, in and out, and his breath hissed faintly around the imperfect seals of his lips and her sex: he perfected them, and she awoke.

He cunnilingued her bearishly, slobberingly, as though feasting upon sweetness, famishedly deconstructing the elegance of his habitual technique, and she shrieked superflux of pleasure, as though to open the flesh of the air for blood and soothing of the scalding delight that possessed her. She jerked and hauled against the bonds, learning a core to her ecstasy from the razor cuts of the silk on wrists and ankles.

Beneath his lips and tongue, her clitoris had hardened almost to bone or enamel, as though in half-anticipation of his intentions. He narrowed the circle of his lips upon it, sucking as though to draw it up and out by the roots, a blind bud sprung somehow from the fertile venereal mont, and closed his lips upon it, nipping, and had added to the sweet sea-stink of her pleasure the sea-rocking of her thighs, rolled from side to side around his head in ecstatic protest.

He bit it off.

For a second her ecstasy remained, embrittled by the impossible agony, and she shrieked again her superflux.

Superflux of pain.

He was already gobbling his way into her, blood hosing hollowly into his mouth, he swallowing a chunk of her flesh that writhed with separate life upon his tongue even as his teeth tore more of her away, the swollen lips of her labia, open on the silent screaming mouth of her vagina; as he fastened his teeth higher, over the urethral meatus, her bladder was released, arrowing boiling gold upon him as though to pierce his brain with compassion. The acrid tang of her piss seasoned the iron of her blood; he paused for a moment, opening his mouth on the spurting fluids, and plunged forward again, opening her like a ragged flower around the flower-throat of her introitus.

At writhing wrists and ankles, blood streamed, bracelets of white bone opened in her white flesh by the grey silk bonds; her face was frozen upwards, jaw dropped dislocatingly far to accommodate the opening of her other mouth, as vociferous as the first beneath his teeth was silent. There were no tears in her eyes; she was far beyond tears, lifted on his eating to an anti-olympus of agony that her eyes seemed to strain to see, piercing thin reality for the über-realities he taught her, squelchingly beneath her single scream.

He was *within* her now, half his head buried between her thighs, his hair and neck and shoulders completely soaked with her blood, which poured out around his working jaws in jets, like the rays of a liquid sun.

By the time his teeth grated upon an inner wing of her pelvis, she was, surely, dead: the blood streaming from the eaten-out core of her penetralia had lost all arterial force and she had ceased to scream long before.

He sat back on his haunches, all his head and shoulders red-thick with blood, lifting one arm and beginning to button the sleeve.

He looked up the bed to see her dead face, and she was still alive, her face frozen into her scream, saliva streaming from her mouth down her right cheek, and her eyes rolling beneath closed, purple lids.

He clicked his tongue with surprise, completing the rolling back of his sleeve, and knelt forward again, pushing his hand between the flopping petals of the gaping flower-mouth he had opened.

Her breasts did not rise or fall, and the hot interior of her body lay still around his forced-in hand, but she was alive.

His fingers, squelching and burping blindly forward through the gap in her pelvis, brushed the fat slick shapes he sought.

He hauled her out.

Her guts.

She steamed, lying stinkingly coiled in the enclosure of her thighs.

And she lived.

He reached forward again, gripped and pulled, emptying her.

The curve of grey silk above her belly settled in time with his outhauling hand.

And she lived.

Third and final time, in the stink of a tropical abattoir, he reached within her, and the fat pouch of her stomach came free with muffled snaps of tissue.

He planted it atop the heap of intestines.

Fluids streamed from it.

His distorted reflection sat on its shiny, steam-wisped surface.

He tore at it with his fingers, feeling scalded with its heat, and dabbled the rich churned slime within it for the two halves of the key.

He lifted them, holding one in each hand between fore and middle fingers, and spun his wrists back and forward quickly to shake them clean.

"Happy now?" she asked.

He leaned sideways for a patch of unsoiled bedcloth, and cleaned the halves of key.

He held them up, matching one against the other, narrowing his eyes against the blood that streamed down his face.

"And me?" she asked.

His hands were beginning to sting with the acid of her stomach.

FROM THE UNPUBLISHED COLLECTION "DCLXVI"

He pulled his handkerchief from a pocket of his trousers and carefully folded it around the two halves of key.

"*In hoc signo*," she said.

He unfolded the handkerchief, and the key was whole.

"There is a sword in the cupboard," she said.

The stroke fell cleanly, hissing. But from the stump of her head and neck no blood flowed, but a waxing luminescence, like a light released from many centuries sealed in darkness, until the room swelled and grew huge with brightness. And then the head, sprouting broad metallic feathers that glittered and flashed in his eyes like death, rose from the bed and flew, chiming the approach of her vengeance.

Her eyes broke open like seeds and her lips writhed independently of the words he heard.

"I give you one minute. Then I kill you. Find the mechanism of my power if you can. Fifty-nine. fifty-eight..."

He screamed. "Ruth!"

From below, broken like crystal with pain, the voice of the lamia rose, and he left the room boundingly, flinging aside the sword and raising the key into its place and shouting to drown the boom of the counting. He swung astride the bannister and slid, fearful for his testicles in disremembering of a banister knob, *whoosh* to the bottom.

The clock in the scullery.

Forty-three, forty-two.

The clock in the scullery.

Thirty-eight, thirty-seven.

The clock in the scullery.

Twenty-one, twenty.

The clock in the scullery.

Sixteen, fifteen.

The clock in the scullery.

Three, two.

The clock in the scullery.

He thrust the key into the lock.

And turned.

The minute hand trembled a second short of eighteen minutes to three.

Above, an over-ripe fruit thudded to the floor of the bedroom.

He stripped and washed himself at the sink of the scullery, pouring freezing water onto the blood with which he was covered as though in ritual laving: water spread wide over the stone floor, pink and pink and pink in the flaring of light from the lamia's entorturement. The window of the scullery looked out over the kitchen garden and when he was done he climbed through it, dropping silently into the rows of vegetables there and running stooped for the cover of the trees.

The second interview with Philomel Thanatophore:

"It is finished."

He pressed the key into her hand and she lifted it to her mouth, smiling. Her lips closed, and she swallowed.

He bent her forward over the table before the narrow rectangle of window, and lifted the grey prison cloth of her skirt.

Sight of the white globes of her buttocks brought him up in a heartbeat, straining against the buttons of his trousers, and he released himself, smiling a little at the eagerness with which his cock jerked forward.

He did not moisten her, merely pressed down harder on her shoulders to bring her up and to him, and left his hands in place, trusting to his luck to guide the blind bald head to the entrance.

His luck was good.

For a moment he held himself back, glans pushed gently to the hot coin of her anus, reporting two hard tiny crumbs of faeces on the rim; and then he pushed forward into the tightness of her bowels.

As he worked at her, mixing pleasure for himself in the mortar of her body with his pintle-pestle, he pondered the significance of the faecal crumbs.

And realized, a moment before orgasm, that if one took her anus as the face of a clock, the crumbs read eighteen minutes past nine.

"Hatred is more than love, always," she groaned beneath him.

He shaped his mouth to speak through the outgoing gasps of orgasm; then, remembering the lamia, narrowed it again, and said nothing.

AARON WILLIAMSON

CACOPHONY #1

Erudition? Yes!
it's cultivated,
ventilated,
"I-the-crashed-accomplice"
a dread miserable
peopling the stars;
a dull brother,
an old shot,
a snapped barrel in the
fright bite:
a *mind*
with a *head*
of its *own*...
RRRROOWWW
C-C-C
"O tain, O tainy,
roo ca ra ca roo coo"
now riven in twain
betwixt head and toe,
between heart and foot
and whittled to this splinter,
thus fracture,
this thisness within a rupture

FROM "CATHEDRAL LUNG"

wherein an utterance is

balanced:

"it must be frustrating"

– mmust be mmutterance

cut up into verbiage,

the depot-fat serum plenary

heaven

of filth and oblivion,

an other-worldly bone-transmittor

scraping

below foliage:

"we can't say it,

we can't be it,

we can't *mean* it"

– it must be in here...

"it can't be said here

at all"

CATHEDRAL LUNG
(Excerpts)

In a room surrounded by at least two masochists, I have to try and shoot my way out says an imitation voice of what could be taken for god in an accelerating series of subtitles... "I have to try and talk my way out"

Tongue
pulls along
pulleys, tarpaulins and traps
bolted to nets and levers
leaving a grey-black hammer metallic
grease
    behind;
the whole thing
        groaning
the whole thing
        breathing ballast,
a snail slides toward daylight
tunnelling iron
into the roots;
winches hoisting the
dead mass of dead purple
weight
on to the silken weight
of lips that languish,
lying there,
      pululating,
         flicking

– and then it entered into my throat.

FROM "CATHEDRAL LUNG"

★ ★ ★

Layers heave an internal web, dead wheels of fortune churn, in urgency, hysterical, a saffron sun in cycle with the trinities of freaks splashed out at intersecting grids and networks; writhing, flashing.

Molecules burn out. A substrate warm mosaic transforms the panic into optical sensations, these accompanied by manacled anguishes of suffocation.

Transparent grating sounds screeching impeccably. A thread of panes cross-sect precise disembodiments of frost as swollen developments of insects colonise the permeable clamour.

Inside the stellar vagus vault, the flayed tongue is painted with menstrual flake. A gong is pulverised.

The silence begins.

FROM "CATHEDRAL LUNG"

CACOPHONY #5

Clenched teeth
the soil twisted
dark vitals maimed
rocks snapping...
a head raised to the angle
of a long-range weapon;
the expiration of exhalation
and a sadist bursts forth
into foul sweet smithereens:
"and why all this violence
against language?"
– abused because innocent,
unabled
of the meaning
protruding from its neck
groping
and snapping
its way to the navel:
"what other navel can there be?"
what other *world*
but this muscle/head
hurts
along the circumnavigation

of these teeth

over

and over

in the same

twitch of the stars

operating the hideous threads

into external meatus,

malleous,

incus,

HAMMERING.

CACOPHONY #8

"like committed pedagogy
when it lit up my eyes"
– and the whites of its thighs
are infested with beeswax
and black pores
the spores of a summer's skies
"I'll never trust a man who lies"
or never trust
the oscillation between polarities
announcing life:
the struggle between blood
against algae
"you mean death?"
"I mean Satan is a selection
amongst Satans"
– it's exasperating
the harmony
into one little mention
of unreality
and then it all riddles out
like something
from the matrix world
retaining its character

but no longer matrichal:

O mol de

O mol da

So mol dah...

now populating into a forgery

a templet of poisoned sweat

founting from bottomless

indigo ancestors

that cloy in the heart:

a glutomate cohesion and dynamism

that's all a mistake

a fat stake:

it's the flavour of

con/flict

CACOPHONY #2

wrench elevator

the brute force

ignites up the clamour...

"listen neighbour,

it's becoming plastic –

here's the inside out;

a meaty hammer"

... and the jurisdiction of life

and pulp fiction about

delicious switchback

vitriol dice;

a universe of lucid dogs

GRRINDING

"I haven't read any of it yet"

and of course more winding

into a cross-section

of gases

rotating

in monochrome

and fed upon stark echoes:

"...wipes clean the yellow slates

of stars once more!"

– it's a flat contra diction

FROM "CATHEDRAL LUNG"

"well no, it's neither, it's just

a piece of fiction

and therefore nothing"

(is represented in full)

"or is that cohesion?"

like the black swarm

stares down

into re-opening lesions;

hungry and hatching

for action...

"are they the brute force?"

CACOPHONY #3

"I don't eat meat I AM meat"

– my own carcass

"you mean sarcophagus"

...contracting,

colliding...

"and the division between flesh

and celestial"

we term *thinking*

is confessed down

intentions

in fact run down

or *thisappeared*

in inking

simply piled up in tensions:

"I won't mention, I won't capture

old nothingdown...

" like steel twisted

crust crystal

galactose, digested,

arrested

in mucous spleen coprophal rings;

flash-scattering

boneyards

of fat and mucin,
old meat femur,
a neat cleavage,
the way you fracture
at the fatigue
– it's slackening:
"it's within talking distance."

CACOPHONY #18

Glossolalia klaxon

a follicle cactus

extracting from scratches

the citrate dirt

veiling

and shunt-biting

through tattooed-tip cuticles

of pulverised front grinders

exhaling refractions

light-resonant

past colon-cog seizures

& dovetailed with

cross-cellular gnashing

at shadowless

yet sustenant flat idols

stab-thundered

through plasmatic damagers

some reverb-cack dendraxons

of amethyst

incision

farfalla

rough haulage scaling drag

wedge-pounding subactions

FROM "A HOLYTHROAT SYMPOSIUM"

of apparatus pincers

the main-tail idalia

hybridising

of ice-claws

and horses

O ye who make haste

to pass through

hell so slowly...

bewailing transactions

and scorching the helium

of lexical aliens

inhaling the breath

of these words

it is fading

too long for this whorl

ACELDAMA

A word that speaks from its quagmired ditch: ACELDAMA

fields of blood

the umbilical spit of blazing streams

creamed and warm, a fossilised infinite vehicle of dreams

captured in tegument

skin constraining the leaping crimson

under the bludgeoning tilt of the skies

the needlework of scriveners dipping within

filtering out of its milk and semen

spit

drawn off, choked and strangling

the wipe of it, smearing multiple chins

cut

unleashed into the breath

into a skein of blood

thickening its plasmic surface

and the quill is loading the fortified pneuma

FROM "A HOLYTHROAT SYMPOSIUM"

and the ink is mixed at the mount of the neck.

ETYMOLOGY OF SCREAMS

The text is born of yearning. It accumulates the need. Pain is stacked through its racks, stratified. The hidden veins are old wounds, wounds that won't wash, won't even show themselves, so tremulous and vulnerable. Cuts to the hand, invisible, yet still there. Unwashed. The clag of guilt for feeling the pain. The text collects it, consists in it. Sometimes the pain is glimpsed, re-limbed, only for the soul to retreat, slammed shut.

The hurt derives. The hunger, wanting to be held. Shut off the need to shut down the pain. To alleviate: the writing about something. Previous to the hurting, that something itself, written. The struggle to read it back again, to unearth the corpus. Unearthly treasure, writ large. Attempting to exhume but merely imitating the sense of loss. I need. The need itself. Autonecessity. The hurt if unmet. Shut down the pain from the hurt and then rip, tear me out.

Symbolic gratifications. Each time, the hopelessness of never being loved. As good as gold and valueless. Someone, anything else, I become. Feeling the way through urination. The shallowness of breath. A face exhibiting to the window. Entering the state of alert, this will always be so: I am detested. To shut down. The balance lost. I was shattered, realising I could be killed. Scattering the target – me – before they got me.

This I know: a system of many-selves. One for who I am and others for those who are not. I am fading. The details of life are clenched to me. Frustrations. The spite I live, I live in spite. I don't like me as I am liked, I don't like them, they don't like me as I am. The end.

But always awaking again, locked away with the pain. Entombed. Years to exhumate the fear. I stank of fear, my liver spitting it out. The stink enticed corollories, I cultivated hurt. There was a way in to the hurt and a way out. Trying to get in or out, to reify the struggle. It killed me, is killing me. I killed me before anything could reach me first. Submerged my face until no breath. The pain is what kills but without it also is death. Me, murderer of mine: guilty. I did it.

FROM "A HOLYTHROAT SYMPOSIUM"

FROM TRASH TO TREASURE
(Excerpts)

The voice which usually refers past itself, trapped in floccule, begun quarranty, escapes through assembling extensions. Prosthetically, a small key hooked at the tip of its internal shape. Not thinking itself. But thinking itself unthinking.

Silence is what we say when we mean what we don't have to say it with. Silence is what we say we mean when we say that we don't have it. Silence is a saying which means very little.

'Don't touch it'. In quotes lies the exterior to utterance, the side from which it turns still through unknowing. Apostrophe is insignia to contain by, to continue with languaging captivity.

Ingrained in this measure: a sonic lash forlorn in the dear date of its unfolding desire.

PREVIOUSLY UNPUBLISHED

A linguistic cast of intentions and tensions: where some say mountains, others see valleys.

Civic bells, engoldened tongues. Who could begin with what is here being said? Believe what is here being said. Belief around saying. A rind. Rind worn outside itself.

Composing ontologies of spinal flack. In speaking be coiled around newly stripped gravity. Dream charts begin with the gist here disactioned.

Begin again with a saying. Conducted, recruited into a line between distinct opposing directions. Simultaneous, discrete. Head off to where the line could be charged through its full range and extent. No longer (than) merely moments being tipped.

Movement and inflexion perpetually subverting intention. Not merely at the surface mouth but in a crucible of phlegm shaped to each extracting word.

PREVIOUSLY UNPUBLISHED

Although the text is semantically fixed, it is only proportionate to these interventions in affording their anchorage.

The true saying of saying: 'everywhere else is pretty big around here.'

Talking, speaking, arguing. Ending, incrementing, instigating. Abrupt, gagging the substance around its life, the voice as not solely a suggestion but an ingestion.

I remember this voice. This membership of the voice is me. I am the voice's own memory. Remembering who I am gives voice here to this. Here is the voice that remembered itself as me. This is me, the voice of memory remembering itself as me in the voice.

What can be meant when we say language? Impossible not to have a limit within, not to have a selective defense in the infinite eye. 'Surdity saw me otherwise.' Alive/to/a/selective/discourse.

A CREATION BIBLIOGRAPHY
1: 1989—1994

ISBNS

(Prefix **1** 871592)

00 3	**RAISM**	James Havoc
01 1	**POEMS 1827—49**	Edgar Allan Poe
02 X	**RED HEDZ**	Michael Paul Peter
03 8	**THE BLACK BOOK**	Tony Reed (editor)
04 6	**BODY BAG**	Henry Rollins
05 4	**THE JACKASS THEORY**	Henry Rollins
06 2	**CATHEDRAL LUNG**	Aaron Williamson
07 0	**CEASE TO EXIST**	A Creation Press Sampler
08 9	**RED STAINS**	Jack Hunter (editor)
09 7	**PHILOSOPHY IN THE BOUDOIR**	The Marquis de Sade
10 0	**SATANSKIN**	James Havoc
11 9	**THE GREAT GOD PAN**	Arthur Machen
13 5	**BRIDAL GOWN SHROUD**	Adèle Olivia Gladwell
14 3	**BLOOD AND ROSES**	A. Gladwell & J. Havoc (editors)
15 1	**KICKS**	Jeremy Reed
16 X	**INTERREGNUM**	Geraldine Monk
17 8	**A HOLYTHROAT SYMPOSIUM**	Aaron Williamson
18 6	**CRAWLING CHAOS**	H. P. Lovecraft
20 8	**KILLING FOR CULTURE**	D. Kerekes & D. Slater
21 6	**ED GEIN - PSYCHO!**	Paul Anthony-Woods
22 4	**RAPID EYE 1**	Simon Dwyer (editor)
23 2	**RAPID EYE 2**	Simon Dwyer (editor)
26 7	**DIARY OF A GENIUS**	Salvador Dalí
30 5	**MEATHOOK SEED**	J. Havoc & M. Philbin
32 1	**STARRY WISDOM**	D. M. Mitchell (editor)
40 2	**HOUSE OF HORROR**	Jack Hunter (editor)
43 7	**ANGELS FROM HELL**	Mick Norman
50 X	**THE VELVET UNDERGROUND**	Michael Leigh
60 7	**THE SLAUGHTER KING**	Simon Whitechapel

2: 1995—96

BRIDAL GOWN
SHROUD

Fiction & Essays
by
Adele Olivia Gladwell

SatanSkin

per ardua ad fussam

James Havoc

a
HOLY
throat
SYM
POSIUM

★ *aaron williamson* ★

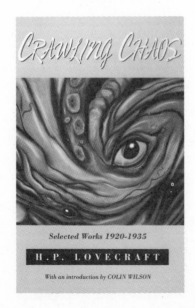

CRAWLING CHAOS

Selected Works 1920-1935

H.P. LOVECRAFT

With an introduction by COLIN WILSON

KILLING FOR CULTURE

An Illustrated History of Death Film
From Mondo to Snuff

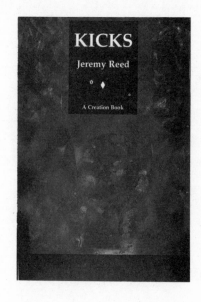

KICKS

Jeremy Reed

◇ ◆ ◇

A Creation Book

RAPID EYE

RICHARD KERN · JORG BUTTGEREIT · GENESIS P-ORRIDGE
THE OTHER BISEXUALITY · SERIAL KILLERS & TWILIGHT LANGUAGE
ALEX SANDERS · PAUL MAYERSBERG · SAVOY BOOKS
TRAVELOGUE USA · AARON WILLIAMSON · H P LOVECRAFT
And much more

RAPID EYE

KATHY ACKER · WILLIAM S. BURROUGHS · ALEISTER CROWLEY
BRION GYSIN · DEREK JARMAN · CHARLES MANSON
PSYCHIC TV · HUBERT SELBY · AUSTIN SPARE · COLIN WILSON
ALCHEMY · HITLER & UFOS · MESCALIN · TATTOS & PIERCING
And much more

HOUSE of HORROR

The Complete HAMMER FILMS Story

DIARY OF A GENIUS

Salvador Dalí

⁹INTRODUCTION BY J G BALLARD

The Starry Wisdom

★

a tribute to H P Lovecraft

★

edited by D M Mitchell

J G Ballard
William S Burroughs
Ramsey Campbell
David Conway
John Coulthart
Michael Gira
Rick Grimes
James Havoc
D F Lewis
Brian Lumley
Alan Moore
Grant Morrison
Robert Price
Stephen Sennitt
Don Webb
Simon Whitechapel
Aaron Williamson
and others

ANGELS FROM HELL

• MICK NORMAN •

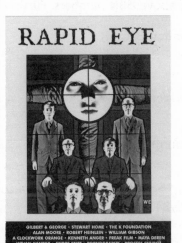

RAPID EYE

GILBERT & GEORGE · STEWART HOME · THE K FOUNDATION
ALAN MOORE · ROBERT HEINLEIN · WILLIAM GIBSON
A CLOCKWORK ORANGE · KENNETH ANGER · FREAK FILM · MAYA DEREN
ISTVAN KANTOR · ANDRE STITT · PORNOGRAPHY · PROCESS CHURCH
And much more

CATAMANIA

THE DISSONANCE OF FEMALE DISSENT
ADÈLE OLIVIA GLADWELL

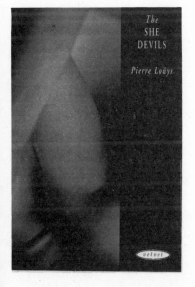

The
SHE
DEVILS

Pierre Loüys

velvet

PHILOSOPHY
In The
BOUDOIR

*The Marquis
De Sade*

velvet

CREATION BOOKS should be available from all good bookstores. Please ask your local dealer to order using the above ISBN numbers. Further information is available from:

Creation Books, 83 Clerkenwell Road, London EC1, UK.

Tel: 0171-430-9878 Fax: 0171-242-5527

A full catalogue is available on request.

Distributors to the book trade:

BOOKPOINT, 39 Milton Park, Abingdon, Oxon OX14 4TD.

Tel: 01235-400400 Fax: 01235-861038

Non-book trade and mail order requests:

AK DISTRIBUTION, 22 Lutton Place, Edinburgh EH8 9PE.

Tel/Fax: 0131-667-763197

Distributors to the American book trade:

SUBTERRANEAN COMPANY, PO Box 160, 265 S. 5th Street, Monroe, Oregon 97456. Tel: 503-847-5274 Fax: 503-847-6018

U.S. non-book trade and mail order requests:

AK PRESS, PO Box 40682, San Francisco, CA 94140-0682.

Tel: 415-923-1429 Fax: 415-923-0607

Canadian distributors:

MARGINAL, Unit 103, 277 George Street, N. Peterborough, Ontario K9J 3G9. Tel/Fax: 705-745-2326

Australia and New Zealand:

PERIBO PTY LTD, 58 Beaumont Road, Mount Kuring-gai, NSW 2080.

Tel: 02-457-0011 Fax: 02-457-0022